Far From Their Eyes

Ohio Migration Anthology

Lynn Tramonte, Editor

Volume I

OHIO IMMIGRANT ALLIANCE

Anacaona LLC

Far From Their Eyes

Editor Lynn Tramonte
Production Editor Awa Harouna
Contributing Editors Shari Nacson and Kevin Tasker
Illustration by Eldis Rodriguez-Baez

First Printing, 2021

Published by Anacaona LLC for Ohio Immigrant Alliance

To Fatiha, Issa, Saidu, Pedro, Jesus, Abdoulaye,
Goura, Seyni, Esmeralda, Moussan,
Ibrahima, Mory, and Amadou.

To your families and your futures.

CONTENTS

CONTENTS

Preface

Alabama and Argentina. Cleveland, Columbus, Cuba, and Czechoslovakia. Guinea, Haiti, and Kent. Mauritania and Mexico. New Jersey, New York, Panama, and Romania. Sierra Leone and South Sudan. Youngstown and Vietnam.

What comes to mind when you read these words? Do you picture far-away places, or see "home" (or both)? Is this a jumble of countries, cities, and states that are very different from each other—or are they also, possibly, the same? Find out as you read *Far From Their Eyes: Ohio Migration Anthology, Volume I.* Each story, essay, painting, and poem in this anthology is rooted in at least two worlds—the physical place its creator is in, today, and the place from which they and their ancestors came.

When I first saw Eldis Rodriguez-Baez' painting "Bleeding," I couldn't get the vivid colors and lines out of my head—and the tiny boats that people from Cuba, Haiti, Mauritania, and other countries use to reach a different future (or die trying). People are fleeing from countries that raised them, and literally bleeding (dying) for a chance at a future other than the one into which they were born.

We were looking for a cover image for this anthology and rejected "Bleeding" at first because it depicts the Cuban flag, and we wanted to be more inclusive. Then, we noticed something. The Cuban flag looks a lot like the Ohio flag (and the Puerto Rican flag), colors inverted. The wrecked boats can represent the various dangers people face when forced to migrate—whether they literally die at sea, like some migrants today and Africans during the transatlantic slave trade, or are killed by violence and disease, like Native people in the United States, and others struggling to survive today.

There. We had a cover that communicates the message of this anthology, exactly. Regardless of where we were born or how long we lived in the United States, we have some things in common. The flags that symbolize our origins, and are meant to be a source of pride, resemble each other. The push to migrate—north, south, east, or west, to a new country or a new state—is a universal human experience and a journey fraught with risk and danger.

We also found our title in the pages of this manuscript, because it spoke of another universal truth: that we only see what we choose to see, but we can choose differently.

In his essay "How Did It Start?" Sony Ton-Aime talks about how "foreignness" can be found even in one's own country of origin. And again, that migration is a constant in the history of humankind, across cultures, regions, religions, and time. He writes:

> For immigrants and foreigners like me, we know where it started and where it will end. It started in our backyards, thousands of miles away from the rich and well-protected western borders.... And if history is any guide, we know it started well before that, way when our forefathers watched powerlessly as those who enslaved them took everything they built, put them on a boat, and shipped them to a place far from their eyes.

What is far, and what is close? That depends on you, the seer. Are your eyes open? Are you locked in searching for differences, or can you see what we have in common—across borders, religions, ages, genders, abilities, and everything else?

Near or far, we see what we choose to see.

Lynn Tramonte
Cleveland Heights, Ohio

Land and Ancestral Acknowledgement

We offer this volume to the world, acknowledging that:

Because of colonialism and supremacy, Ohio's Native peoples survive only in the names of places and rivers today. The word "Ohio" is derived from the Seneca word "Ohiyo," or "beautiful river." Ohio was once the beloved home of Erie, Kickapoo, and Shawnee people. Members of the Delaware, Miami, Ottawa, Wyandot, and Seneca (Mingo) tribes migrated to Ohio after white colonizers pushed them from their original homes. In the 1800s, all were sent west by the occupiers of stolen land.

While some of our ancestors came here voluntarily, others were forced to leave their places of origin. Houleye Thiam says: "For Black Mauritanians, migration is not a vacation. It's not a choice. Dictators are weapons of mass destruction." Mauritania has its own colonial racism that forces many to leave and make Ohio their home. Other ancestors came to the U.S. in chains (or not), to work in homes and fields, construct railroads, and build and care for this nation. This labor-based migration continues today. Paid little despite their essential place in society, these workers deserve to be acknowledged with dignity.

Ohio will not be a "free state" until all people are truly free. Our history books proclaim Ohio was a "free state" in the 1800s. Stops along the Underground Railroad are treasured landmarks today. But descendants of slaves who migrated to Ohio still face a state culture of white supremacy and an official government that does not value their lives. Ohio is “home” to many racist, anti-Semitic, homophobic, Islamophobic, and anti-immigrant groups and people, as well as the police officers who killed Tamir Rice and Andre Hill, among many others.

Ohio must confront our past and present honestly, and recognize that we are all just people, with equal worth and dreams.

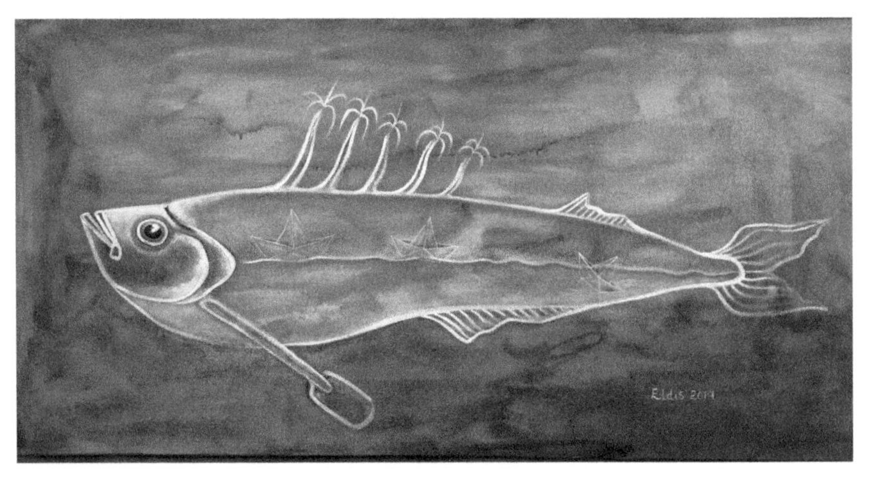

The Chronicles of an Immigrant
Eldis Rodriguez-Baez

Bol Aweng

Bol Aweng is one of the Lost Boys of Sudan. At the age of six, he was forced to flee his village and travel 1,500 miles on foot to a refugee camp in Kenya. Bol eventually came to the United States. He graduated from The Ohio State University, majoring in fine art, and was awarded the Robert Duncan Alumni Citizenship Award for starting the Buckeye Clinic in South Sudan.

Bol lives in Hilliard, Ohio with his wife and five children. He speaks to thousands of students each year, sharing his story and raising funds for his clinic.

Discretion is advised. *The Journey of Hope* has themes of violence and death that may not be suitable for all readers.

1

The Journey of Hope

I was born in southern Sudan, Africa. At the time Sudan was the largest country in Africa, but my village, Piol, was tiny. I enjoyed carefree days taking care of my family's cows, like other boys my age. I belong to the Dinka tribe. To the Dinka, cows are so important. Boys often went far away to the river to find water and good grass for them.

But in 1987, when I was six years old, civil war broke out in southern Sudan. Soldiers came into Piol firing weapons. My people were shocked to find that there were bombs coming from the sky and tanks rolling across our once-beautiful fields. The people were frightened, and it was total chaos. Terrified, I ran away like many of the boys in my village. Even the animals were fleeing.

I thought I would go somewhere to hide, and my people would come back. But the village was on fire. All we could hear was the sound of guns. My village was decimated by the enemy. I wondered if I would ever see my family or home again.

Although I did not know it yet, my life would never be the same.

I ended up walking away from my village. I searched for a safe place, but there was none. The soldiers were everywhere.

I did not know where I was going, so I followed other boys who were looking for a safe place. I began a long journey with thousands of other "Lost Boys." We walked for miles and miles, for days and days, weeks and weeks, months and months. The environment was so hostile to us. Some boys were so exhausted that they could not make it across the desert. The lack of food and water, and the heaviness of our sorrows, made it difficult to continue. We tried our best to carry those who couldn't walk, but some of my friends just couldn't go any further.

They did not make it. Barefoot and with almost no food and water, I walked for over seven weeks looking for a place without war. Within days of beginning the journey, we were starving. We had to eat wild leaves, fruits, roots, anything we could find. We had never tried to eat these things before, but we needed to stay alive. As we walked, we also had to fend off wild animals. Lions were one of the common animals that we faced along the way. When we saw a lion, the only thing we could do was to come together in a tight group. Together, we tried to appear larger than the lion and scare him away.

Eventually, we made it to Ethiopia and our numbers had swollen to 35,000. The people who had hunted us could not cross the border. When we arrived, however, there was no room for us in the refugee camp. We had to build our own shelters and gather food. They gave some the duty to cut grass or to cook. I was the leader of a group of a hundred boys.

After we built the shelters, we built a school. But in the meantime, we met outside under the shade of a tree for our schooling. Education was important, and it kept our minds occupied. We learned English and math under the trees. Our teachers tried to help us rise above our situation, so that someday we could return to Sudan as educated leaders.

Throughout the journey, we did not have a building or any holy place to worship. So, we used the shade of trees to have our service. We studied the Bible, prayed, and sang songs of praise. When we were under the trees, the military helicopters could not see us and bomb us. We felt we were on a journey like in the Bible. Like God's people, we were traveling in the wilderness. We took courage from that story.

In the refugee camp, though, we finally did not have to worry about meeting together. Sadly, after about four years living this way, war came to Ethiopia. We had to flee again. The soldiers tried to force us to go back to Sudan, which meant crossing the Gilo River, which was swollen with the heavy spring rains. Behind us, we heard gunshots from the soldiers. I was not an excellent swimmer, but I had no choice but to jump into the river's dangerous and strong currents. The current dragged some. Those who could not swim drowned, "just like that." Crocodiles killed others. It was a terrifying time and the longest moment of my life. As I struggled against the raging water, I discovered I had somehow reached the other side. Though I was exhausted, I ran as fast as I could go.

We lost about two thousand that day because of the bullets, crocodiles, and dangerous currents of water that carried my friends away. That day I lost many people I loved.

Thousands of us had just crossed the desert, and we were finally close to Kenya. We had come so far and didn't have the energy to look for a safe place to sleep. So, we lay down in a dried-up riverbed and tried to get some rest. In the night, the soldiers ambushed us while we slept there in the open. I heard gunfire. I was disoriented and tired. I couldn't figure out which direction the shooting was coming from.

I woke up and found myself soaked. I could smell the blood. I felt myself, then saw that my friend, sleeping beside me, was dead. It was his blood that had sprayed on me. Many died that way.

Although we had already spent so many years running, once again we were forced to flee, this time to Kenya where the enemy was not allowed. It was a three day, non-stop walk to the border. We had no shoes, and the road was very rocky. When I saw the sign welcoming us to Kenya, I felt like I was finally breathing fresh air. I was so relieved that the soldiers could not follow us to that border. I hoped we were finally going to be safe.

We lost many of our friends because of the gunshots, hunger, river crossings, wild animal attacks, and dehydration. Out of the 35,000 boys that set out on our way, only 16,000 made it to the Kenyan border. Nineteen thousand died along the way.

I spent fourteen years in refugee camps in Ethiopia and Kenya. I lived in miserable conditions in these camps, with hundreds of thousands of other refugees. I slept in a three by four meter shelter with my cousin, Jok, and shared meager rations of corn flour and lentils. Deprivation, disease, and death were everywhere in these camps.

Then, one day, we were told that we could apply to go to the United States as refugees. I filled out an application and had several interviews. I waited and waited. It took three years for my refugee application to be approved. One day I received a letter that said I was going to be "resettled" in the United States.

On my way to the United States, they delayed my flight in Amsterdam. There seemed to be much confusion and worry. It was very hard for me to figure out what exactly was going on. The date was September 11, 2001: the day terrorists attacked the Twin Towers in New York.

Did they attack because I was going to the United States? Do I follow war, or does war follow me?

Eventually, I flew to Nashville, Tennessee and was resettled there as a refugee. Later, I transferred to The Ohio State University. When I became a U.S. citizen in 2007, I decided I could now return to my homeland.

I had heard that my parents were alive, and I wanted to reunite with them. I stayed for a month and saw the terrible living conditions of my family. When I returned to Ohio, my cousin Jok and I decided that our "journey" would continue and become one of hope.

Our journey back to Sudan helped us realize we could change lives in our country through building a much-needed medical clinic for women and children.

I realize Americans do not know about the struggles and sufferings of my people. The problems in Sudan are not reported and are "hidden," as if in shadow. Horrible events are still occurring in South Sudan. I have told my story in churches, schools, and throughout the community to bring to light what I went through and what my country is still experiencing.

My story had touched many, and many joined me to make my dream a reality. Over several years, many people gave their time, prayers, and financial support. A committee helped me organize and start the Buckeye Clinic in South Sudan. Students helped raise funds to build the clinic.

Today the Buckeye Clinic is helping to improve the lives of my people and giving them *hope!*

The Journey of Hope
Bol Aweng

Michele Rudolph

Michele Rudolph is a professional Storyteller and teaching artist. She uses storytelling to share the lives of African American men and women, like her family who left the south to build new beginnings in the northern cities.

Michele lives in Cleveland, Ohio and is a retired social worker.

2

Cleveland, The New Promised Land

Private Ethan Henry Washington could not believe his ears, The War was over! Three long bloody years and now, thank God, the war was over. Ethan, like most Negro soldiers fighting in the Korean War, joined the army for a better job, good pay, and to get out of the south. The black soldiers from the south had been sharecroppers and farmers, all of them trying their best but without gain to scratch a life out of the southern soil their ancestors toiled, planted, and harvested.

When the Korean War began, it sounded like a way out to Ethan and the Negro sharecroppers, and for three years it was. Ethan saw all kinds of death and destruction in Korea, but now it was back to Alabama, another kind of war and death. Returning to the south was the death of the black man's spirit, potential, and pride. In Alabama and throughout the south, black men and women were being terrorized, jailed, and lynched for minor infractions or for doing absolutely nothing. Most of the Negroes living in the south were surviving on little or nothing and living under the thumb of the Jim Crow laws.

Ethan had big plans. He had sent some of his pay back home to M'dea to help with his seven sisters and brothers. With the money he saved for himself, he planned to move to Ohio and get a job in one of the factories that was hiring Negroes from the war. Ethan's cousin, Howard, and his wife Loretta, had already moved to Cleveland and got a job, a place to live, and a brand-new car; a 1953 Chevrolet. Howard even sent Ethan a picture of the shiny, baby blue car. Howard had written to Ethan and told him that life was much better for Negroes in the north, and Ethan could stay with him and Loretta until he got a job and up on his feet.

They honorably discharged Ethan from the United States Army on December 17, 1953. He returned home to Prattsville, Alabama and bought a one-way train ticket on the L&N railroad to Cleveland, Ohio. He felt guilty leaving his family and Anna, his girlfriend, so soon after returning from Korea. But he knew his family would benefit more if he got a job and could send money back home. Ethan would send for Anna as soon as possible, so they could be married and begin a new life together in the promised land, the north. Cleveland, Ohio.

Ethan's cousin, Howard, met him at the train station in Cleveland. It was December, one week before Christmas. It was cold, windy, and snowing. Ethan had never felt such cold before and was not dressed or prepared for this climate. This type of cold, and certainly not snow, did not exist in Alabama. He knew it would take some getting used to. But right now, he was so cold, he could feel the icy cold traveling to his bones. Thankfully, Howard had extra warm clothing for him, or he surely would have frozen or at worst, gotten sick, which would have delayed his plans to find a job and send for Anna. He already missed her like crazy.

Howard and Loretta lived on a street lined with tall trees that looked to have hundreds of houses covering both sides of the street. They built the houses very close together. The neighborhood was an all black community called Glenville. Some of the houses were duplexes where different families lived upstairs and downstairs or side-by-side.

Howard and Loretta's house was a side-by-side where you entered the front door and then went either left or right depending on which side you lived in. The house was much larger inside than it looked from the outside. You walked directly into the living room, then through the dining room. The two bedrooms were off on the side of the dining room, down the short hallway. The small but ample kitchen was in the back of the house. Howard introduced Ethan to their next-door neighbors, Bernard and Joyce Thompson, and their two sons, Kevin and Lil Bernard. Bernard Sr. worked second shift at the steel mill.

Early Monday morning Ethan was dressed in his only suit, which he wore to church and funerals back home. He was ready for his job interview with the foreman at Republic Steel, which was the fifth largest steel mill in the country and the largest employer in Cleveland, and they were hiring Negroes. Howard had been working at Republic Steel for a year and a half and was doing very well for himself. Ethan was willing to work hard to make a good life for him and Anna.

Republic Steel hired Ethan as a Laborer, working in the pit where the steel was melted and formed into steel rails to be loaded and shipped nationally and internationally. The work was physical and hard, and the heat was stifling, but the pay was good. Ethan was able to send for his Anna.

Ethan and Anna were married May 23, 1954, in the home they shared with their cousins Howard and Loretta. It was a simple ceremony with the Preacher, Howard, Loretta, and their next-door neighbors from the Thompson family.

Everyone in the neighborhood came from somewhere, and everyone worked to have more than they had. These brave people migrated to this new land, Cleveland, to be free from fear, to work, to build communities and educate their children, to have a better life and a brighter future. Ethan and Anna had six children, all born in Cleveland, the new Promised Land.

This story is inspired by my father, Eddie Rudolph, who fought courageously in the Korean War, left Alabama, moved north to Cleveland, Ohio, worked in the steel mills, married my mother, Mary Lucille Fields, and raised six children. This is a tribute to him and the six million other African Americans who were a part of the Great Migration.

The Unfinished Journey

Eldis Rodriguez-Baez

Ena Zan

Ena Zan moved to the U.S. from Argentina by herself, when she was twenty-one, to pursue post-secondary education. She completed an Associate's Degree in Hotel and Restaurant Management, and returned to school years later to complete a Bachelor's Degree in Social Psychology. She also went on to graduate school for a Master's Degree in Social Work.

Ena currently works in healthcare, as a bilingual mental health professional. She is married and lives in Columbus with her husband and their sphynx cat, Nico.

3

1,2

#1
My first name chopped,
Mispronounced,
Misunderstood,
Missed.

My last name questioned,
my origin challenged.
My face does not fit their mold.
Could it?
Would it?
Should it, ever?

Nah.

#2
And just like that,
after a 33-hour ride in the skies,
my skin was no longer white.

Skye Nguyen

Skye Nguyen is a seventh grader at Old Trail School. She wrote this essay about her Grandpa, from Vietnam, when she was in the fifth grade. She enjoys writing, flipping, art, sports, dancing, and spending time with family and friends. She was looking forward to going to Vietnam with her grandparents but, unfortunately, the trip was cancelled due to COVID-19. Her mom is also a published author.

4

The Life and Story of My Grandpa

My grandpa is the most inspiring and influential person I've ever met. He inspires me to be stronger and braver. Even though his mom died when he was young, he just recovered from cancer, and he had to leave his country, he is still ready to have fun, get food, and go on lots of vacations. Whenever my family and I go to visit him in Columbus, we always get fantastic Vietnamese food, throw footballs, and do lots of talking. He is generous, brave, fun, and pretty hard to understand. He has dark brown eyes that seem threatening and caring at the same time. After cancer, he had a bald head as smooth as a baby's. He has a warm, friendly smile and a salt and pepper mustache. My grandpa is extremely hardworking. He loves to travel and try new things. He also loves nature and animals.

Living and growing up in Vietnam made my grandpa who he is today. He grew up with his seven brothers, two sisters, aunt, and dad in a few small cottages. He spent his days reading, watching movies, playing soccer, biking, fishing, talking to his friends, and going to school. In his school, there was no P.E, no art, just one teacher and one class. When he was ten, his mom died of typhoid fever. He and his six younger siblings went to live with his aunt.

At his aunt's house it was crowded, not only with siblings, but an interesting array of pets. He had dogs, cats, goats, an otter, and a monkey. The four goats weren't for meat or milk, they were simply friends, pets, and play-buddies. His otter was an Asian Small Clawed Otter, the smallest otter in the world. He would take him outside, walk him on a leash, and take him to rivers so he could catch fish. The otter wasn't good at catching fish, so my grandpa had to buy him some. A tiny, goofy, six-pound monkey lived on my grandpa's porch. His name was Cong Khi, which means "kid monkey." The monkey was a Kong Kei Det Do, which means "kid monkey butt red." My grandpa would feed Cong Khi bananas, papayas, and coconuts.

Grandpa studied biology and chemistry when he went off to college. He wanted to be a professor, and did so well on his exams that they offered him a scholarship to medical school. His dad encouraged him to be a doctor. My grandpa went to medical school at the University of Saigon, one of only two medical schools in the country.

It was at medical school that my grandpa met my grandma, Nhi (whose name is now Sarah). Nhi, a pharmacy student, went to the medical school to find out if her brother had gotten accepted into the university. There, she saw my grandpa. As he said, "She instantly fell in love with my sweaty, curly hair and intelligent, handsome looks." My grandpa invited her out for a Coca-Cola (he paid). A week later, he stopped by her apartment. She offered him longan fruits, an orange, and tropical berries. "I fell in love with her too," he told me. They got married two years later on January 12, 1974.

At the end of medical school, my grandpa was drafted into the Army. He attended classes for four months to learn how to be an army doctor before escaping Vietnam. By then, South Vietnam was losing territory. Saigon was being shelled by rockets and IEDs. My grandpa's brother-in-law, Allen, was a Lieutenant in the Vietnamese Navy. It was becoming obvious that Saigon was going to fall. One day, a Navy captain told Allen he could bring family on a boat to escape, but they had to leave that night. For my grandpa, it was a fairly simple decision to leave, but the hardest part was being unable to contact his and his wife's family to let them know. Little did they know, three years would pass before they could let them know they were okay.

For my grandpa, leaving Vietnam after spending the first twenty-seven years of his life there was the hardest thing he ever had to do. On April 29, 1975, my grandpa, grandma, and Allen boarded Navy ship HQ505. Grandma Nhi/Sarah was six months pregnant with twin boys. As they were leaving the harbor, Saigon was being attacked and bombed. They brought only a small duffel bag to America with some clothes, a watch, cigarettes, and film with pictures from their wedding. They had no money. On the ship, there were no baths, and they ate army rations. During all the time on the ship, my grandpa spent his time trying to help anyone who looked sick, since he was already a doctor.

The ship arrived at an American Army base in the Philippines on May 6, 1975. From there, they took a container ship to Guam, where they stayed at a refugee camp for about a month. My grandpa said, "I was not scared. I was young and figured all I could do was take it one day at a time." On June 2nd, they flew from Guam to Honolulu, Hawaii. Then they made their way to San Francisco, California, and finally to the Fort Indiantown Gap refugee camp in Pennsylvania. Three days after arriving, Grandma went into preterm labor. The twin boys did not survive.

When my grandpa first arrived in America, his starting impression was that it was humongous, and that the people were very compassionate and considerate. They were taken in by the Diamonds, a sponsor family, in Hershey, Pennsylvania. A sponsor family is a family that takes refugees into their home until they can find a place to stay. Describing the Diamonds, he said, "They were poor, but had good hearts."

The first job my grandpa managed to get was as an orderly in a hospital. The local church helped him find this job. The only problem was that while he could read English, he couldn't understand it when it was spoken. Over time, he learned to understand English by watching T.V. shows like *Walter Cronkite* and *Columbo*. It took about two weeks before he realized he could understand the language. Grandma and Grandpa stayed with the Diamonds for two months until they saved up enough money to get their own place. My grandpa was very interested in learning the new culture and lifestyle because he always liked to learn. When I asked him what it was like adjusting to the new way of life, he said, and I quote, "I was not lost. It was... Okay."

While my grandpa was working as an orderly at Lebanon Valley General Hospital, he eventually got his first paycheck. He used the money to purchase a book called *Harrison's Principles of Internal Medicine* to study for the exam required to be qualified as a U.S. Medical Graduate. My grandpa passed both the medicine and English proficiency exams in September 1976.

Then, they accepted him into a residency program in emergency medicine in Barberton, Ohio. When my grandpa was working as a resident, there were other guys with the same name as him, so he had his name legally changed to Harry (the name of one of his sponsors in Pennsylvania). Also, his Vietnamese name was spelled P-H-U-C, so you can imagine how that could go very wrong.

I have never met anyone more determined and brave than my grandpa. He became an emergency medicine physician and later specialized in addiction medicine. He had two sons, my Uncle Nick and my Dad, Tom. My grandparents now have two homes, one in Columbus, Ohio, and another in San Jose, California.

Some things my grandpa most misses about Vietnam are the weather, the music, and the view. His favorite season is the rainy season (in Vietnam there's only a rainy and dry season). His favorite place there is a small town called Soi An. The town has old historical homes and a covered bridge built by the Japanese.

My grandpa's favorite food is *pho*, which is basically Vietnamese beef noodle soup. My grandpa first went back to Vietnam after thirty-three years in America. Now, usually about once a year, we see photos on Facebook of him and my grandma feeding crocodiles, canoeing down rivers, or just chilling on a beach in Vietnam. Sadly, he couldn't do much traveling recently since he got diagnosed with cancer. Luckily, he has recovered, and my family and I look forward to going to Vietnam.

My grandpa has had an extraordinary and very interesting life.

Skye's grandparents, Sarah and Harry
Their engagement party, 1973

Alejandro Virgo

Alejandro Virgo is a Brooklyn, New York native, educator, poet, and amateur photographer. Born to immigrant parents from Panama, they instilled in him the value of education, hard work, and leadership. He obtained his Bachelors of Art in Communications as well as his Masters in Public Health and Nursing. His primary areas of focus are program analysis/evaluation and infectious disease burden.

Virgo hopes to merge the two degrees to aid marginalized communities. He is very passionate about incarceration practices and poor health outcomes in marginalized communities domestically, as well as WaSH (Water, Sanitation, and Hygiene) and neglected tropical diseases in low and middle-income countries. Beyond his professional pursuits, the arts have and will always be Virgo's first love.

He currently lives in Cleveland, Ohio.

5

Tidal

A journey to turn negatives into positives
But in the downpour, it seems the silver lining tarnishes
I brave seas of doubt only to find jagged rocks of insecurity on her shores

As waves crash violently against my vessel, I capsize
Navigating, I can't blame the sea for the shipwreck I realize

The current pulling me closer to her sanded beaches
As I touch down on solid ground I build monuments to compliment her, and appease

Tremors move Earth and turn my work to debris
I fall to my knees at the water only to see no reflection
Cracks in the water distorting images of the sky
The moon in the heavens, while the pastel blue paints
pluvious portraits of a sunrise

Only eclipsed by the horizon, imperfection she sets her eyes on

Whispers in the wind turn calms into a raging tempest
As I seek shelter in her palms, my only focus is survival

Just when I made this hell a home,

I get washed away by waters tidal

Cuba

Eldis Rodriguez-Baez

Nanette C. Auerhahn

Nanette C. Auerhahn, PhD is a clinical psychologist and psychoanalyst in private practice in Cleveland, Ohio. Currently, she teaches at the Cleveland Psychoanalytic Center and the Department of Psychiatry of the Cleveland Clinic.

Dr. Auerhahn is a child of Holocaust survivors and grew up as a first generation American in Brooklyn, New York. Her mother was from Czechoslovakia, and her father was from Romania. After surviving numerous concentration camps and losing most of their families, they spent years trying to be admitted to the United States, where they finally met.

Dr. Auerhahn published numerous articles and book chapters on trauma. Since 2020, she has been co-chair, with Ira Brenner, MD, of the American Psychoanalytic Association's annual discussion group on the Effects of the Holocaust and Genocide on Survivors and Family.

Discretion is advised. *On Being a Child of Holocaust Survivors* has themes of violence and death that may not be suitable for all readers.

6

On Being a Child of Holocaust Survivors

Arriving in Auschwitz, my mother watched as a truckload of children were dumped into a bonfire to burn to death. Suicidal, she began to bang her head against a wall. "What do you see that I don't see?" implored her thirteen year-old niece beside her. What had driven my mother to despair was recalling her father's teaching that every human being was created for a purpose. "For what purpose were these children created?" she wondered. I hated this story as a child, because it confronted me with the possibility that life has no meaning.

Eventually, my mother was transferred to work near the gas chambers in an area called Canada, because of its bountiful collection of belongings that had been brought with arrivals to the camp. It was the work of the Canada Commando to sort through these belongings. My mother had been lucky to get this assignment, as it was a position that allowed the opportunity to sometimes pilfer extra food hidden among the packages. "It might help you survive," offered the kapo doing the assignment, "but you will curse me for it."

Being next to the crematoria and the site of medical experiments on twins and other detainees, she could have no illusion as to the fate of most inmates. In close proximity to the killing center, my mother watched as the Gypsy camp was murdered as well as most of Hungarian Jewry.

The husband of one of my mother's sisters was chosen, along with an acquaintance from home, to work in the crematorium in a brigade called the Sondercommando. The young man, whom she knew, told her that her brother-in-law had "lost his mind" when coming across the corpses of his wife and children. The night before the men of the Sondercommando revolted and blew up one of the crematoria, this individual came to bid his sister, my mother's co-worker, goodbye: "For tomorrow I die."

The men knew that their revolt was hopeless. When it failed, several ran to the Canada Commando and hid among the packages, only to be rooted out and shot in front of the women of Canada, who were lined up before a firing squad. In the last minute, the officer in charge of the women recanted the order, but all had to watch the hanging of those women who had helped smuggle gun powder to the men.

During her time in Auschwitz, my mother tried to ascertain the fate of her sisters' twins who had been taken from their mother upon arrival. She was never able to determine if they had been experimented upon, but to the end of her life, my aunt retained the 'hopeful' fantasy that rather than be killed, these children were experimented upon and somehow survived. She imagined that they were alive somewhere, not knowing how to find her because they had forgotten their identities.

These twins were never spoken about in my family, but throughout my life, I harbored a secret fantasy that I would bring them back to life. When I became pregnant with twins, a cousin called me and admitted to having had a similar fantasy and to having always wondered which one of us would give birth to twins.

A few years ago, when I learned of a movie about the Sondercommando called *Son of Saul*, I resolved not to watch it, especially after starting to view its trailer online. The trailer was so evocative that I quickly burst into tears and turned away. When asked to write a discussion of the movie and other films about the Holocaust for a book on Holocaust cinema (Auerhahn and Laub, 2019), I forced myself to watch it, but could barely do so. Months later, when I was asked to discuss the movie at a conference, I considered watching it a second time but couldn't bring myself to. During that period, I had the following dream:

There were several glass bottles with the invisible bodies of people in them. Slowly, life was fading out of these bodies as they suffocated to death. One could tell because although the bodies were invisible and indeed were essentially wisps of air, so long as the individuals were alive, the color in the bottles was pinkish red. As the individuals suffocated, the level of red became lower and lower until no color remained once the person inside had died.

I watched this process happening and quickly grabbed one of the bottles to pour the person out, because the red had almost disappeared. I could neither see nor feel his body, but followed the instructions of a figure who told me to conjure up the body through my hands. I massaged what I imagined must be there, believing in the experience of my mind and putting on hold my absent sensory experience. Very slowly a body began to emerge, first in black and white and finally in color, with clothes. But it was dead and try as I might, I could not revive it. As I awoke, I had the thought that I wanted to dream the dream again to attempt once more to resuscitate the individual who had died.

I share this dream as well as my avoidance of the movie because they illuminate aspects of my relationship to the Holocaust. I had few associations to the dream and felt estranged from it, as if it had come from somewhere else and it was not I, the dreamer, who had crafted it from my own experience. As my first viewing of *Son of Saul* had been six months before, I did not connect the dream with either the Holocaust or the movie. It took over a month to do so, and only after my therapist reluctantly shared what she thought were her associations only, that the dream was connected to the Holocaust.

Her hesitancy speaks to the difficulty of bringing horror into an intimate relationship and the shame and sense of isolation associated with acquaintance with trauma. When she did share her association, in a manner parallel to the role of the dream figure who aided me in trying to bring an individual back to life, I remembered a number of brief associations I had had to the dream but had quickly set aside and forgotten.

The presence of another person as a validating witness is crucial to the ability to own what one knows of trauma. A veil lifted, and I remembered that I had formed a brief visual picture of crematoria chimneys when visualizing the bottles, and had pictured peoples' remains wafting through those chimneys. The sense of being trapped and suffocated in the dream recalled my childhood fantasies of gas chambers as well as my catastrophic reaction to the claustrophobic image from *Son of Saul's* trailer, the fire and heat of the crematorium.

I associated the attempted resuscitation of the dead body in the dream to the revival of the boy who survives the gas chamber in *Son of Saul*, while I connected the wish to dream the dream again to revive the dead with the ability to rewind a movie and watch it again. Such a redo, of course, defends against the finality of the real experience, which cannot be undone. Rewinding also evokes the experience of post-traumatic stress in which trauma is relived over and over again.

The dream image of thrusting my mind into an experience not embodied in my sensory registry conjured up both the engagement through the imagination engendered by movie-going, as well as my terrified childhood memories imagining my family's experiences in the gas chambers. As a child I had imbibed my survivor parents' experiences without going through them and without even knowing them consciously, grieving a past I had not lived through, just as in the dream, my hands acted as if they experienced something they could not verify as corporeal but nevertheless trusted as there, because of the narrative of another person.

Is this not my experience as a child of survivors who is haunted by a history that is not my own? It is especially the case of young children of traumatized mothers who imbibe the visceral experience of trauma with mother's milk, honing close to the experience of dreaming, as I did as a child whose mother not only worked next to the gas chambers in the Canada Commando, but whose father lost a wife and child in

Auschwitz. A child imbibes a parent's trauma via imaginative participation and implicit, unconscious processes, living a past that she never experienced. This is eerily not unlike our dream experience, which we live in our minds, without physical enactment. I have come to see my dream as depicting, through images and sensations of suffocation and vaporization, a depressive mood related to terror of the soul dying.

As a psychologist and researcher, I have written extensively about trauma. Much of my work was originally conceived in dialogue with the psychiatrist Dori Laub, himself a child survivor of the Holocaust. When my younger son, Ben, began to walk before the age of one, I remember him teetering quickly, wobbly, on the verge of imminent collapse, trying to carry his father's work satchel. The briefcase was big and heavy and weighed Ben down. But it was clear that he felt he was holding on to something that would give him support, even though the opposite was true. The actual briefcase, as opposed to whom it represented, hampered and destabilized his flight.

A story told by Yaffe Eliach in Hasidic Tales of the Holocaust (1982, p.4) comes to mind. Inmates in the Janowska Road Concentration Camp were made to jump a huge pit or be shot. Among them was the rabbi of Bluzhov and his friend, a freethinking Polish man. After they both successfully jumped over the abyss, the Polish man asked, "Tell me, Rebbe, how did you do it?" The rabbi answered, "I was holding onto my ancestral merit. I was holding on to the coattails of my father ... my grandfather and my great-grandfather, of blessed memory ... Tell me, my friend, how did you reach the other side of the pit?"

"I was holding on to you," replied the rabbi's friend.

When I work with trauma, I need to hold onto someone, lest I fall into an abyss. When I've written about trauma, I have sought out coauthors. When I work with asylum seekers (as a psychologist doing psychological evaluations of immigration detainees), the collaboration with immigration lawyers is crucial for my mental health. And when I work with victims of abuse in my private practice, I sit with a hot cup of coffee in my hands to warm my insides lest they freeze from horror; I conjure up the companionship of my mother and aunt who used to gather around the kitchen table for a cup of coffee.

I have come to understand survivors' attempts to freeze out their inner worlds as efforts at warding off despair, disintegration, and suicidality. Deeply defensive and continually triggered, reminded of murder, mayhem, and losses, my parents tried to protect me from knowledge of evil, but otherwise had little place left in their minds for their own child's mind. While twinning and mirroring build relationships, my parents were deeply private and secretive, making our relationships feel like no relationships. I was unable to match my parents' scary interior with their words and behavior and was uncertain as to whether the danger I sensed was inside or outside.

My parents' minds inside my own created a phobic response to my own mind, which I unsuccessfully tried to protect from my parents, coming with bodily memories of torture and tragedy. My parents were inarticulate, their stories replete with gaps and hidden places, so that I could not tell what was secret, what was private, and what was unspeakable. I think of my own depressed periods as an incorporation of something inedible and toxic from them. Picking up on my parents' unconscious without their permission, swallowing their externalizations and projections without my permission, I have spent much of my professional life sorting out the intergenerational transmission of the sensorimotor inscription of trauma, coming to recognize that our sense of the world comes from a shared interpersonal reality that includes intergenerational lived experience.

History is constructed out of what we address with others, ideally giving words to trauma which otherwise can be experienced as undigested, wordless bits of bile that are vomited onto others lest they choke us.

The world that I inherited from my parents was marred by worry that others will attack because I had no right to be there. A world where hatred and genocide occurred and still occurs has felt like a dog-eat-dog, cannibalistic world filled with continuous shame, where people experience each other as objects and destroy each other. For me as a child, it was a world lacking in spontaneity and flow—an upside-down world in which I was unable to make the fine distinction between exposure to the psychotic part of the mind and being psychotic.

Survivor parents often cannot process emotions because they are unable to tolerate emotional links that feel like too much. As a child of survivors, I anticipated that relationships require consent to carry a burden. I was unable to know that I was separate from grief, which fragments and resembles a toxic state—like a poison. My parents had so many losses that they could not prepare me to master grief and move on. Instead, I would get stuck in anger and depression.

To know that life was mine to grasp, I had to leave home behind without the baggage of my parents. This required the ability to grieve, say goodbye, and own my aggression which had often been set aside when dealing with suffering parents.

As a graduate student, I interviewed Holocaust survivors as part of a video archive project. By hearing others describe external events, I finally was able to locate the horrors I had imagined as a child outside myself, realizing that I was neither crazy nor bad for having imagined such unspeakable events. I had been uncertain as to whether I had the right to explore my fantasies about my parents' experiences, because of my shame for having such thoughts. For children of survivors, the mortification their family members endured can give rise to shame for looking at their own private qualities, their own subjective life, and their family's private life. Shame, in turn, can re-trigger trauma, as it represents the threat of social death—the possibility of again being dehumanized, objectified and made, as Nazi doctors described Jews, a "life unworthy of life" (Lifton, 1986).

Trying to heal my parents as a child has evolved into treating trauma victims as a therapist and working politically against current injustice—my way of bearing witness and giving meaning to life—thereby realizing, finally, the potential of mourning.

Fishing Illusions

Eldis Rodriguez-Baez

George Shadrack Kamanda

George Shadrack Kamanda is a master's student of diplomacy at Oxford University and a third-year law student at Case Western Reserve University. He is a civic educator, human rights advocate, and published author of three books.

Kamanda is founder and executive director of the Necessity Firm, a citizenship firm in Sierra Leone. He immigrated to the United States from Sierra Leone in 2012, and volunteers his time with non-governmental and civic organizations helping immigrants from all over the world settle in America.

7

Homeless

Some have detached roofs over their heads.
Some have broken bricks to cover their homes,
while others are moving about in disarray—
Just like the lives they live,
and that a spectacular display of the lives they live.

From sunrise to sunset children rattle their parents for food.
From morning to night backs and feet are tied in the forest and yet,
harvest season blinks like a beaming headlight.
symbolic view of their everyday lives.
At nights, they lay on filthy streets in the mornings,
they meet terrible conditions,
All just to make a way.
And yet, they continue to hustle in strenuous
ways with signs of progress far away and
this is the reality of their humanity.

Bleeding

Eldis Rodriguez-Baez

Houleye Thiam

I'm Houleye, a Social Worker by day, an interpreter by night, and a community organizer in the afternoons and on weekends. Yep, I'm busy, but it's a "good" busy.

I'm busy making a difference in people's lives, and I would not have it any other way; I was born to do this. I'm originally from Mauritania, West Africa, and I currently live in Columbus, Ohio.

I hold a Bachelor's Degree in Social Work and two Master's Degrees, one in Public Administration and the second in Human Services, with a minor in Community Leadership.

I'm currently the Executive Director of two nonprofit organizations, Youth and Hope and the Mauritanian Network for Human Rights. The first assists children in Mauritania to go to school by providing them with school supplies. The second advocates and provides services for Mauritanians living in the United States, and raises awareness about human rights abuses in Mauritania.

My passion for social justice dates back to when I was five, when I saw my dad getting hand cuffed and taken away by the racist government in Mauritania, simply for having the courage to speak about racial discrimination. In my high school days, I was the only girl in a class of twenty-four and I had to stand up to bullies early, because my survival and success in school depended on it. I love organizing for a better world, where human beings are treated with fairness and justice, no matter the colors of their skin and their backgrounds.

8

Three Poems

My Accent

On this chilly January morning I have something on my mind,
which is my accent, the way I sound when I talk, as in the *accent* I have,
the accent you may or may not have.
How I sound when I speak, when I speak English.
I have heard it all.

Huh?
Wait, say that again...
Oh, you have an accent!
Can you repeat that?
You have an accent? When did you get here?

I wonder how many people believe that only people from other countries have accents. People in the same country living in different regions can have accents that differ from each other, as much as they differ from those of people from other countries.

You may notice this.
For example, someone from New York may sound different from someone from Ohio,

And someone from Texas may sound different from someone from West Virginia.

OK, back to my accent.

Sometimes when I talk, people don't understand what I am saying.

Note, I said sometimes. Sometimes they are fine, but sometimes they aren't.

Especially when I use long sentences, or words such as "gubernatorial"

Whether the person has known me for a while or just met me, I always get

What's that
What did you say?

And I have to repeat myself two or three times before the other person

Can understand what I am saying. That moment, when the other person is asking me to repeat myself, and I am repeating myself to be heard and understood,

That moment can be very uncomfortable for us both.

Often, our conversation stalls on this roadblock. The other person will look up,

Not trying to continue the conversation,

Sometimes out of fear of offending and saying the wrong thing

Sometimes because they don't feel it is worth the effort.

Often in these situations, to avoid continuing this conversation, they look up,

Look down,

Act as if they understood what I said

Just to avoid asking one more time.

But others push on, even though they know I may just say something else

That they do not understand. And when they choose to continue the conversation,

They are in for a treat!

When they push on, that is when they get the story behind the accent.

That is when I get to tell them that this accent is me. This accent is

Mauritanian, Senegalese, New Yorker, and Ohioan.

This accent is a Social Worker by day and an interpreter by night.

this accent is Issa's mom,

Diyena's sister,

Samba's daughter,

Mamadou's cousin.

This accent is a human rights activist

And a social justice advocate.

This accent is a high-heels hater, green-color lover.

This accent is a product of four languages

From Fulani to Wolof, passing by French and English.

This accent is the story of survival in immigration.

This accent is nonprofit executive, Youth and Hope President.

This accent is Natasha's Case Worker, Jasmine's Personal Advocate.

This accent is a poet and a storyteller. This accent is the seed of endless possibilities.

Yes, this accent is me, all of me, and I am a work in progress.

When our leaders are preaching about building walls, we can choose

Not to go that route.

We can instead choose to build bridges, and we do so by using these uncomfortable moments.

When we do, it gives us the opportunity

To cross the divide and connect on our humanness. Reaching out to others can be scary.

This world of immigration and movement can be scary.
But you know what Mandela said—
Courage is not the absence of fear,
But the ability to push on despite that fear.
So I challenge each one of you:
Choose courage over fear,
Push on beyond your comfort zones.
A world of connections and discovery awaits.

The choice is yours.

Have We Arrived?

Have we arrived, one might ask
Now that we can work and pay taxes
Now that we have won the battle for voting rights,
After many fights

Now that we have been able to work full time,
Now that we have been putting in our time,
Now that we have been able to go to the moon
Although it all seemed so soon
Now that we can join the armed forces,
Now that we can ride the horses,
We have come a long way indeed.

We got here because many sacrificed their needs
Have we arrived, one may ask?
Women's rights still seem like a monumental task
So many questions that need to be asked
We are still in a lot of fear.

Even after Obama signed Lilly Ledbetter
Because right after Obama
We got the other of version of Osama
No, worse, this one is not hiding in the Middle East
He is a beast

To him, women are only good for a feast
He has no regard for Roe v. Wade
To him, all that is retrograde
What do we do, one might ask?
Oh, it all seems like such a task.

Fight!
Strike!

There is so much at stake
In the hands of a man who is oh, so fake
But a woman is as tough as a nail
She is on his tail
She might fail
But every time she will get back up
And pull herself by her bootstraps
She is always ready to take on another battle
For her rights, she will never settle
Freedom is what she desires
To her liberty she aspires
Currently everything she cherishes is under fire
Safety is never safe
She will not cave
Security is a myth
But she is swift

She will keep fighting for all of her sisters around the globe
Because she knows they are closer to her than her ear lobe.

Dare to Hope!

She is an epitome of strength
The cornerstone of resilience, she has travelled the distance,
despite the length.

She is the missing rib of Adam
the link between the past and the future
they taught her to only be the phantom, the ridicule, and the satire
She is the reflection of all that is wrong
in our world against which she stands for
despite all the uproar.

She is a Hillary Clinton,
Daring to become the leader of the free
world despite the double edge standard.

She is an Angela Merkel,
who took in refugees despite her lowest ratings

She is a ROSA PARKS,
who refused to get up despite her fears of what may just erupt.

She is a Fatima Mbaye,
Who refused a prize a from racist President
because she believed in a Mauritania
where racism was not rampant.

She refused a prize of honor
from a president that took pride in dishonor.

She did not ask for this struggle, she did not begin it
But she intends to win it,
Even if she has to go through all of this trouble.
And today of all days,
we celebrate her,
We honor her.

#PushingForwardDespiteTheChallenges Queen H~

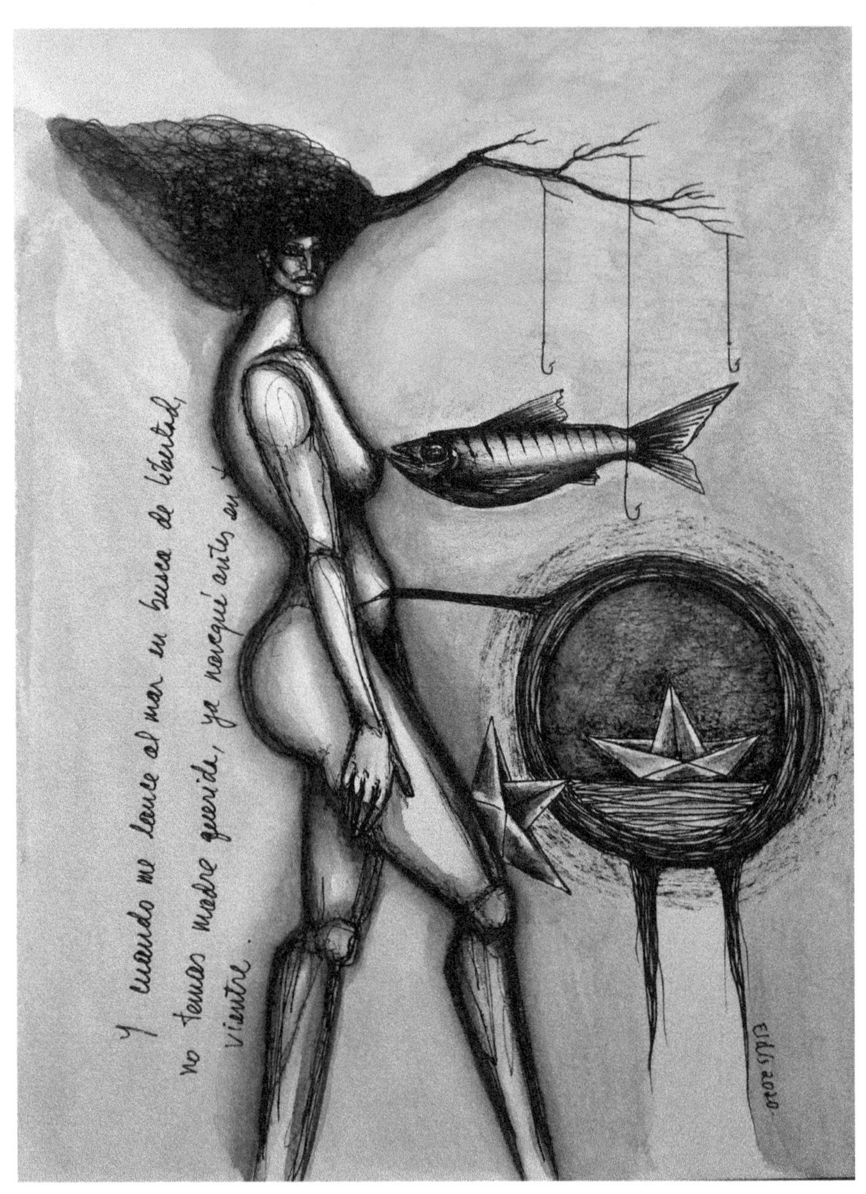

Uncertainty

Eldis Rodriguez-Baez

Sony Ton-Aime

Sony Ton-Aime is a Haitian poet, essayist, and translator. He is the director of Literary Arts at Chautauqua Institution and holds an MFA in poetry from the Northeast Ohio Master of Fine Arts program at Kent State University. Ton-Aime is the author of one chapbook, *La-Womann* (Ironworks Press, 2019) and a translation of the book *Olympic Hero: The Lennox Kilgour's Story* in Haitian Creole. He is the co-founding editor of the ID13 Prison Literacy Project.

9

How Did It Start?

Two years ago, my then seventeen year-old brother called and told me he thought a smartphone would do him some good, which was his way of asking for one. I told him no. Categorically. I was staggered by what I understood then to be a vain and irresponsible demand. How could he ask me for something so luxurious as a smartphone, when he could ask for many important things? For example, I knew his motorbike needed new tires and his school tuition was coming due. But two weeks later, when I called again and he explained why he needed it, I realized that like it was for me in the U.S., a smartphone had become a basic need for him as well.

I asked myself, when has a phone become so commonplace that a seventeen year-old Haitian could not live without it? How fast things have changed! What a strange place the world has become. I also remembered seeing similar changes when I was growing up, but none like what my young brother was experiencing.

When I was eight years old, I would go to the countryside on New Year's days. I would bring my mom's *soup joumou*, first thing in the morning, to my uncle's family. In turn, they would send me back home with enough food for our evening's dinner. I always needed the strongest mule to carry all the food. That was the time when you could still ride a horse into town.

New Year's Day was my favorite because I got to spend it with my twin cousins. They were just one year older than me, but I worshipped them. They could do all the manly things that I could barely do. They could recognize a bird by its tweet, knew what leaves to use in a tea for a stomach ache. They climbed trees like spiders. They knew when the rainy season would end and when the moon was ripe enough to put the plantain stumps in the ground. But all they wanted to talk about were the stories from my books.

When I turned fourteen, there was no countryside to go to anymore. Not that the place vanished, but there were no people left there that I knew. All my relatives had left and moved to the town, which was being called a "city" by then. I did not understand why they left. They did not understand it either, I believe. I wished they never did. I missed dipping my toe in the cool river during these winter days, running in the sanding field, feeling the mounds of the peanut plants under my toes, and mostly, I missed the fresh air of the country. Of course, I am being romantic in my nostalgia. Of course, life was not all that rosy. I am sure my mother and my uncle would remember these times differently. But in my carefree childhood, I was happy, at least during those New Year's.

My uncle's family moved to my city with its loud motorcycles and kids who would call you by your first name, no matter how old and respectful you were. This city was filled with hurried students who would laugh at the way you spoke, yell something in French, and step on your toes without the least regard. This city offered nothing for the soul, but there you could make in one month what you could make in a year in the countryside.

This was my town. I was raised in it, but I did not know it. In one year, my cousins came to know my town better than I ever did in my fifteen years. I was not interested in knowing it. The cities that I was interested in were in my books. They were made of tall buildings. They were covered with snow during Christmas time, and their stores were buoyant with white people buying gifts. One wishes for things that one does not have. Same as a country Ohio girl wishing for life in the big city, my cousins were wishing for a life in my city, while I was wishing for a place with an endless number of books and snow. Everyone has a wish in place. Only some must leave their countries to find it.

For most westerners, Americans and Europeans, immigration either starts with the news of caravans or boats heading to their borders, or it is a distant reality that lives in their parents' history. This makes it difficult for them to see the individual in the crowd. Paradoxically, they cannot see the crowd for what it is either. They cannot see what creates this exodus. This paradox renders their knowledge of the origin of the crisis incomplete, so their solution can only be flawed. Inadvertently, these un-informed and half-cooked solutions perpetuate the crisis.

In Tell Me How It Ends, Valeria Luiselli's daughter asks her how it would end for the immigrants seeking asylum, and Luiselli had no answer for her. How could she have an answer? How could anyone know how it ends without knowing how or where it started?

For immigrants and foreigners like me, we know where it started and where it will end. It started in our backyards, thousands of miles away from the rich and well-protected western borders. It started for me when I became obsessed with the *Adventures of Tintin* and wishing I could, like him, travel and see the world. It started with my uncle's family moving to my town. And if history is any guide, we know that it started well before that, when our forefathers watched powerlessly as those who enslaved them took everything they built, put them on a boat, and shipped them to the place far from their eyes.

When they arrived in my city, my uncle was still tending to his little farm in the countryside, but the revenue from his harvests could not sustain a family of nine in the city. His two oldest sons had to learn to ride motorcycles and they became taximen. They made a deal with a man who had a couple of motorcycles. They both got a motorcycle that they could use from him, and they each had to pay him 500 HTG (roughly $20 at the time) every Friday. They took care of the vehicles. They bought fuel, new tires, brakes, everything that was needed. A taxi ride cost 5 HTG from one place to another, back then. It was 15 HTG to go to the next city or town. No one ventured further on a motorcycle taxi, so 15 HTG was the most one could earn for a single ride.

My aunt joined my mother selling second-hand clothes. My mother did her best to help, but she had difficulties counting money. People took advantage of that. My twin cousins, envious of my ability to read, asked to go to school. They attended the neighborhood elementary school with their younger siblings.

Although four of them were working, the family could barely stay afloat. After buying groceries, paying for tuition fees, and covering the other necessities, there was nothing to save. When the new mayor stopped horses from entering the town except on Saturdays, my uncle had to buy a bicycle, something that he would never have done in the countryside. These things that were luxuries before became necessities.

As Aristotle would say, this is the final cause of the immigration crisis: needs are becoming universal. Neoliberalism with its forceful globalization makes the needs of the poor Haitian the same as his rich western counterpart.

More than half of my high school class left Haiti after graduating. Among those who went away were scholarship winners like me, and the more fortunate with parents with wallets big enough to afford their trips and studies. I was fortunate to attend a prestigious high school which made it possible for me to be part of a special "caravan." If that was not the case, who knows? I might have been one of the four thousand walking their way to the U.S. border almost every month. There has almost always been a mass exodus (caravan) coming to the United States: the Italians, the Irish, the Japanese, the Chinese, the Polish, the Haitians, etc. The response from the established and American-born has always been the same: sheer disgust and disregard for the lives of these people. Never have they asked what is causing this problem.

My dad could have been one of them in the 80s and 90s. Then, it wasn't called a caravan. It was "boat people," mostly from Haiti and

Cuba. Still, some seventy percent of Americans were against letting them in, although they were fleeing certain death from political persecutions. Like the asylum seekers at the southern borders are put in an icebox, the boat people are arrested and sent to prison in Guantanamo Bay, away from the eyes of good, God-fearing Americans.

The scholarship recipients from my class went all over the world: the United States, France, Cuba, Dominican Republic, Chile, Benin, etc. I knew some ten of us who came from my town and only two of us had gone back. It is important to ask why we did not go back. We visit sometimes. It is both good and unsettling to go back and see the reverence and amazement in the eyes of those left behind.

During our few trips back, we would bring the things that are necessities in the U.S. and Europe with us. Necessities like iPhones, cars (we rent those), music boxes, fancy clothes, etc. We bring some to our families and friends, too. They, in turn, go and show them off to their friends. These friends ask their family members in the U.S. to send them some, like my little brother did. What started simply as a way to impress others quickly became necessary to function. Of course, it is not only the fault of the individual. Big companies, through technology and global reach, are playing a big part in the influx in immigration.

A few years ago, I used to buy calling cards to call my family, five dollars for five minutes. Then came apps like Messenger and WhatsApp, and they changed everything. Suddenly, there was no need to pay for a card as long as someone in my family had a smartphone. My older brother bought one and everything seemed to be okay. Then my little sister got one, because my older brother left the house. Now that my little sister is in college in another city, my little brother needs one if I have to talk to my mother. For my little brother, however, it is more than helping me talk with my mother. It is necessary for him to stay connected with his friends. If you do not have a smartphone you do not receive the WhatsApp invitation, you are left out. You need that phone. It is necessary that you get that phone as soon as possible, if you wish to stay in the group.

I know that a smartphone costs almost as much as the average annual income of a Haitian. With that knowledge, how could I be surprised when a 2015 World Bank report stated that nearly sixty percent of Haitians cannot meet their basic needs? Why would I be surprised to see the caravans of people heading to the U.S. southern borders? Why would I be surprised to know that violence is rampant in the southern countries? Why do I even question why I could not go back to Haiti? Why was I surprised when my little brother asked me for a smartphone?

It did not start with my uncle moving to my city or me reading *Tintin,* or end by putting a stop to these things. Maybe the reason that Luiselli could not answer her daughter was because there was not an answer to this question. It cannot end because it is now a circle, a vicious circle.

Luis Héctor Pérez Oliveros

Luis Héctor Pérez Oliveros nació y vivió en Apaseo el Grande, Guanajuato, México. Asistió a la escuela elemental Vasco de Quiroga y cursó la secundaria en el Colegio México en la ciudad de Celaya, Guanajuato. Sus estudios preuniversitarios los terminaría en el Instituto Celayense y tuvo como profesor al distinguido humanista Isaías Lemus. Hizo estudios universitarios en España e Italia y terminó su maestría en español en la Universidad de Akron, Ohio en los Estados Unidos. En este momento hace estudios de doctorado en la Universidad Antonio de Nebrija en Madrid, España.

Actualmente radica con su familia en la ciudad de Strongsville, Ohio y es presidente de "La Mesa Española," una de las más antiguas organizaciones en los Estados Unidos dedicada a promover la cultura y la lengua de los países hispanohablantes.

El cuento "Muerte o Pasaporte / Passport, or Death" fue inspirado por eventos verdaderos. El original es en español, traducido al inglés por Lynn Tramonte.

* * *

Luis Héctor Pérez Oliveros was born and lived in Apaseo el Grande, Guanajuato, Mexico. He attended the Vasco de Quiroga elementary school and the Colegio México in the city of Celaya, Guanajuato. He finished his pre-university studies at the Celayense Institute and had as a professor the distinguished humanist Isaías Lemus. After that, Pérez did university studies in Spain and Italy and completed his master's degree in Spanish at the University of Akron (Ohio) in the United States. He is studying for a doctorate at Antonio de Nebrija University in Madrid, Spain.

Pérez is president of "La Mesa Española," one of the oldest organizations in the United States dedicated to promoting the culture and language of Spanish-speaking countries. He currently resides with his family in Strongsville, Ohio.

The short story, “Muerte o Pasaporte / Passport, or Death,” was inspired by true events. The original is in Spanish, with English translation by Lynn Tramonte.

10

Muerte O Pasaporte

Cuando metí a mi cuñado en la cajuela de mi carro no sabía si iba a aguantar el viaje. La muerte por asfixia es la más común, aunque también la deshidratación y la inhalación del bióxido de carbono suelen ser mortales. La travesía en la cajuela de un carro sería larga y peligrosa. No pararíamos hasta Saltillo Coahuila, México donde se encuentra el último retén. En caso de que sobreviviera, sería el primer alemán que pasó ilegalmente a México.

Este era nuestro viaje de vacaciones a México y debido a que nuestra familia es numerosa, decidimos hacer el viaje en carro; en varios carros.

La historia comenzó cuando llegamos a Laredo Texas, el paso fronterizo que nos corresponde si queremos seguir la ruta federal 85D hacia el interior del país.

Al intentar cruzar la garita aduanal de Nuevo Laredo, Tamaulipas, el oficial en turno no quiso aceptar el pasaporte de mi cuñado. Le pidieron que se bajara del carro y lo metieron en un cuartito sin ventanas que olía a humo de cigarrillo, desinfectante y restos de comida de hace tres días. Había latas de cerveza vacías tiradas en un rincón y una ratonera sin queso.

Los aduaneros leyeron su pasaporte minuciosamente, revisaron cada entrada y salida de los países que había visitado. Examinaron los sellos de las visas con lupa. Cotejaron la edad y la clase de tinta de las firmas. Lo interrogaron como si fuera miembro activo de Al-Qaeda o del Talibán. Al fin de la investigación, el aduanero de turno dijo:

—Este pasaporte es falso. Aquí dice que usted es alemán y usted parece hispano; sus rasgos físicos son de la región de Ixhuatán, Oaxaca pueblo que hace frontera con Chiapas. Además, la foto no corresponde. Es de una persona más joven.

—Mi pasaporte es totalmente legal. Nací en Frankfort el 18 de mayo de 1950 de padre mexicoamericano y madre alemana. Aquí también tengo mi visa de residente de Estados Unidos. No sé cual es el problema —dijo mi cuñado con un gesto de disgusto.

—El problema es que usted no puede pasar a México con este pasaporte falso. Ahora, que si tanto le urge visitar este país pues... nos podemos arreglar.

—¿Arreglar qué? No veo que haya nada qué arreglar. Mi pasaporte está en regla.

—Mire señor, no me haga perder el tiempo. Si no facilita las cosas le sugiero que se retire y se regrese de donde vino.

—Pues no me arreglaré con usted ni con nadie. Prefiero no ir de vacaciones.

Obviamente, Tiburcio Sánchez López, tercera generación en el lucrativo negocio aduanal, quería su mordida.

A las cuatro de la tarde, cansados y bajo el sol inmisericorde de Laredo Texas, mi cuñado, el alemán con rasgos «benitojuarenses», decidió que no le iba a dar nada. Le pedí, le rogué, le supliqué que le diera para sus refrescos, pero no cedió.

—Es cuestión de principios —dijo—. Yo nací en Alemania y allá no se hacen estas cosas.

—Pues..., aquí sí. Aquí puedes cambiar de principios en un instante. En la mañana tienes unos y por la noche otros. La «mordida» es la grasa que agiliza los trámites. Hasta los presidentes lo hacen. Es la tradición. Lo que nos legaron los conquistadores.

—¡Pues no! Ni un centavo para este ratero. Mis papeles están en regla —dijo el cuñado desquiciado por la rabia.

Esperamos hasta la noche y a las once y media metí al cuñado en la cajuela de mi carro. Le di una almohada, lo cubrí con una manta y le di una botella de agua. Mi esposa, llorosa y angustiada le hizo la señal de la cruz a su hermano y no le puso los santos óleos porque no los llevaba. Leí el pánico en su rostro cuando cerré la puerta de la cajuela. Mi cuñado sintió como si le estuviera cerrando la tapa de un ataúd. Apasionado seguidor del cine mexicano sabía de las cárceles mexicanas y por supuesto no quería de ninguna manera ir a visitarlas.

Tiburcio Sánchez López el aduanero del primer turno ya se había marchado, para él, hoy fue un lunes anodino y la pesca de víctimas no había sido buena. Un día entero y sólo robó doscientos veintitrés dólares y cuarenta y tres centavos. Filomeno Gómez Farías —turno de noche— estaba de reemplazo y sufriendo una cruda que le tenía paralizado el cerebro y atrofiados los músculos. Más dormido que despierto no quiso interrumpir su rehabilitación y con una mano y sin siquiera levantarse de su cómoda posición nos dio la señal que siguiéramos adelante. Ninguna revisión. Ningún pasaporte. Nada. Al menos en la aduana fronteriza la habíamos librado.

Cuando llegamos a Saltillo ya habíamos pasado todos los retenes. Paré en «El Osito Dormilón» un motel de mala muerte—quince dólares la hora—para averiguar cómo se encontraba el alemán. No se oía ningún ruido y pensé que se había asfixiado. Pero no, ahí estaba, sereno como angelito y roncando como un político ebrio. Dormía a pierna suelta abrazado a la llanta de repuesto. La libró el cuñado. Pasó los retenes con los ojos cerrados como un perrito recién nacido. Me gustaría saber si es el primer alemán que pasa de mojado a México. Lo despertamos y dijo:

—Estoy todo adolorido, pero por lo menos no pagué la mordida. La corrupción paró conmigo. ¡Hoy es un día histórico! Este país tiene que cambiar. ¿Cuándo será eso? —dijo el alemán con coraje.

—Pues... cuando Jesús venga a resucitar a los muertos tenemos una chance —dije.

Cuando le conté esta historia cien por ciento verídica a mi prima, se le erizó la piel, se le dilataron las pupilas y le corrieron gotitas de sudor frío por el espinazo. Se puso pálida. Se le subió la presión a ciento ochenta y estuvo a punto de desmayarse.

Marta Fidela Buenrostro Centeno es una prima lejana, tan lejana que rara vez se comunica. A Marta Fidela se le casa Juliancito, su hijo menor, en la Riviera Maya; boda a la orilla del mar en hotel de cinco estrellas. La ceremonia será en cinco días y su pasaporte—he aquí la tragedia—está vencido.

—¿Qué voy a hacer? Me quiero morir. Me perderé la boda de mi hijo —dijo y empezó a llorar.

Juliancito, a sus cuarenta y tres años, no quería casarse y se hacía el remolón y para demostrarlo, desatendió sus obligaciones de ayudar a su novia a preparar la boda. Al final, la novia—a quien le faltó un minuto para mandar todo al carajo—relegó todo el trabajo a su futura suegra. Marta Fidela—que lo que quería era que Juliancito se saliese de casa y dejara su cuarto para poder rentarlo—decidió echarse a cuestas la responsabilidad de arreglar los preparativos de la boda.

Reservó el hotel para ochenta y nueve personas; todos los cuartos—a exigencia de los invitados—con vista al mar. Consiguió un padre católico para que oficiara la misa—lo cual, en sí, es un acto épico ya que la mayoría están presos—en la Riviera Maya. Designó el menú de la cena incluyendo a los vegetarianos y veganos, contrató a los mariachis, quienes olieron dólares y le cobraron a treinta dólares la canción, ordenó las rosas a Colombia con cargos extra de importación, mandó hacer el pastel de tres leches y los vestidos victorianos de las damas de honor.

Marta Fidela se hizo cargo de los más mínimos detalles de la boda y la absorbieron de tal manera que lo último que se le ocurrió fue revisar su pasaporte y comprobar que seguía vigente. Presa del pánico y con los nervios a flor de piel llamó al Consulado de México en Detroit y suplicó, lloró, los amenazó y al final les ofreció dinero y aun así le dijeron que no hay citas disponibles para renovar el pasaporte.

—Lo sentimos señora. Ni aunque viniera el Papa Francisco a casar a su hijo podemos hacer excepciones. El pasaporte se da con cita y no hay citas hasta el mes que viene. Eso sí, rece mucho señora a lo mejor alguien cancela —dijo el oficial.

—Ya me cansé de rezar. Se me acabaron los santos a quien pedirles el favor; los volteé patas arriba y la verdad es que hasta estoy perdiendo la fe.

Desde mi punto de vista, a mi prima Marta Fidela Buenrostro Centeno, quien siempre me ha despreciado y me ha tratado como un paria, le quedaban dos alternativas:

Primera quedarse donde está y ver la boda por Zoom.

—¿Cómo se va a quedar Marta Fidela sin ir a la boda sólo por no tener pasaporte? Ella es la madre, y es mexicana cien por ciento. No se ha hecho ciudadana americana porque piensa que es una traición. Va de visita a México, a su tierra natal —dijo con enojo mi vecina Altagracia Revueltas Patiño, quien me hizo el favor de quedarse conmigo a dormir y ahora se ha despertado con los ojos rojos y un greñero de león indomable después de doce horas de sueño.

—¿Y cómo se comprueba que es de México? Con sus facciones autóctonas puede ser de cualquier país de Centroamérica y ahora con lo de la «caravana de migrantes» lo más seguro es que la Migra la deporte a El Salvador, Honduras, Nicaragua o Guatemala. Y la verdad, y sin ofender eso sería peor —dije.

—¿Y cuál sería la segunda opción? —dijo mi vecina Altagracia al momento que recogía su jueguito de ropa íntima regada por todo el piso.

—La otra alternativa es esconderla en la cajuela de un carro y cruzar la frontera, llegar a Monterrey y ahí tomar un avión a la Riviera Maya. Se haría lo mismo que hice con mi cuñado el alemán hace ya varios años —dije con gesto de burla.

—Sí, todo me parece muy bien. El problema es que tu prima ya tiene setenta y cinco años. Padece de ansiedad, reumatismo, diabetes, sólo tiene medio riñón, sufre de presión alta y taquicardia —dijo mi vecina, quien se puso a tender la cama y vi como metió su pijama transparente detrás de la almohada pensando que se va a quedar aquí otros días.

—Bueno... si sobrevive el viaje hasta el último retén, entonces participa de la boda de su hijo, si no pues se suspende la boda y se arregla el funeral. De cualquier forma, la familia estará reunida —me reí hasta que me dolió el estómago.

Entonces mi prima recibió una llamada del Consulado Mexicano en Detroit donde le anuncian que una persona había cancelado:

—Hay lugar para su cita señora —dijo el oficial. ¿A qué santo se encomendó?

—No me lo ha de creer, pero el Santo Niño de Atocha salió al quite —dijo.

Marta Fidela brincaba de gusto y le ofreció al Santo Niño subir de rodillas hasta la ermita, bailar descalza hasta la medianoche y llenar su capilla de flores.

Inmediatamente, Marta Fidela me llamó y me pidió que de caridad la llevara a Detroit a hacer los trámites de su pasaporte.

—Primo tienes que llevarme a Detroit. Me urge renovar el pasaporte. Si no, no voy a la boda de Juliancito —dijo con lágrimas en los ojos.

—¿Y tu esposo? ¿Por qué no te lleva él?

—Ya no ve. No puede manejar. Después de la embolia se quedó chueco, sólo el lado derecho le funciona.

—¿Y tus hijos?

—Ya todos se fueron. Adelantaron sus vacaciones. Mi esposo y yo somos los únicos que quedamos. Teníamos que hacernos cargo de la abuela.

—A mí ni siquiera me invitaron a la boda —dije con un reproche.

—No te dijimos porque pensamos que como estás desempleado no tenías para el pasaje. Y además, acabas de salir de la cárcel. Necesitas disfrutar a tu familia y no puedes salir del país.

—¡Ése era mi problema! De todas formas, me hubieran avisado. ¡Y sí puedo salir a la hora que yo quiera!

—Mira Carlitos, no es hora de cantarme los rencores, ayúdame y yo te pago tu pasaje en avión hasta la Riviera Maya. Estoy desesperada. Sólo tú puedes salvarme.

—Bueno, no lo hago por el viaje, lo hago por ti. Y para que aprendan a no despreciar a los que tenemos contratiempos en nuestras vidas.

—¿Acuchillar a un fulano fue un contratiempo?

—Por favor prima no me juzgues. Ya serví mi condena. Y además sólo le hice un rasguño. Fue en defensa propia.

El viaje a Detroit fue desagradable; una ciudad en ruinas y paulatinamente abandonada. Poco a poco la *Ford*, la *General Motors*, la *Chrysler* y otras industrias automotrices y la ciudad han ido desapareciendo. El centro estaba sembrado de edificios abandonados, tiendas clausuradas, restaurantes con las luces apagadas y los vidrios rotos y un enjambre de mendigos y rateros que rastreaban el centro en busca de víctimas.

—Se parece a Chernóbil después del accidente nuclear —dijo la prima.

—¿Y tú cómo sabes de Chernóbil?

—Lo vi en la tele. En una serie de HBO —dijo y añadió

—Detroit es igualito.

—Si, la diferencia es que aquí los habitantes que quedan no hablan ruso y no los ha matado la radiación.

Debido a la devastación urbana de Detroit, el gobierno de México—siempre alerta para proteger a sus ciudadanos—cambió sus oficinas a Madison, un suburbio de Detroit. Madison es un pueblito de casas ordenadas, con jardines atiborrados de flores, cercas pintadas de blanco, pasto bien cortado y niños que van y vienen en sus bicicletas.

El cónsul, don Rufino Rivera Fuentes, reliquia de los regímenes arcaicos, alquiló un edificio en lo que antes era una guardería infantil abandonada y los burócratas mexicanos—siempre activos—lo acondicionaron como oficinas de gobierno. Quitaron el póster de Mickey Mouse y pusieron el retrato del presidente Manuel López Obrador, removieron a Tribilín, el Pato Donald y Elmo y los sustituyeron por los cuadros de Miguel Hidalgo, el padre María Morelos y el emperador Agustín de Iturbide. Los muebles para los pequeños de la guardería los vendieron en el Mercado de las Pulgas y con las ganancias fueron a un lugar donde venden productos de oficina de segunda mano. El Consulado de México estaba listo para servir a la raza de bronce.

Llegamos a la dirección que marcó el Navegador; Milla Doce 1403, Madison Heights 4807, Michigan. El Navegador «*Maps* de *Apple*» aseguraba que era ahí el Consulado de México, el lugar, sin embargo, era un centro comercial con restaurantes y tiendas por departamento. El edificio del consulado no se miraba por ningún lado.

—Aquí no hay nada de consulado —dije.

—Sigue buscando primo a lo mejor está detrás de Walmart o de Costco —dijo mi prima ansiosa y desesperada.

Buscamos por media hora hasta que vimos un letrero pintado con crayones de muchos colores el cual anunciaba que al fondo, a un lado de Pizza Hut y detrás de Burger King se encontraba el Consulado de México. Vi el edificio y pensé que era una broma. Sin embargo, una bandera mexicana con los colores descoloridos y el águila deshilachada—no había presupuesto para una nueva—indicaba que efectivamente ese era el nuevo Consulado de México. Nuestra representación nacional en el extranjero tenía sus oficinas en una guardería infantil abandonada.

Nos bajamos del coche y nos dirigimos a la entrada principal. En la puerta había un letrero: «Esta puerta no tiene manija use la otra puerta a la izquierda»

Entramos a la sala y parecía la entrada a un cine improvisado. Conté veinticuatro hileras de sillas de plástico de diferentes colores alineadas frente a una pantalla digital. A los lados, en cinco casillas, los burócratas, vestidos con *jeans* y camiseta—era un viernes social—estaban listos para atender a la gente.

Inmediatamente, en la antesala nos saludó un anciano afroamericano a quien le faltaban los dientes del frente. Llevaba barba de varias semanas y un traje negro y roto como si fuera el de un director de una casa fúnebre a quien lo hubiera pescado una tolvanera en el llano de Texcoco. Pensé que se trataba de un hombre sin hogar, un mendigo que buscaba refugio del calor en el Consulado de México. Pero no, era un empleado del gobierno de México, el primer contacto que tienen los visitantes con el gobierno de nuestro país. El africano llegado de Nigeria en un barco atiborrado de café supremo era el edecán atento que le daba la bienvenida a gente de todo el mundo.

El octogenario—para compensar su vestimenta—se comportaba solícito y obsequioso como un asistente de senador federal. El anciano padecía los primeros síntomas del mal de Parkinson y con un ligero temblor de la mano derecha nos ofreció un papel con los nombres de las personas que habían hecho la cita. No encontré el nombre de mi prima en la lista. Enseguida me di cuenta de que la lista era del día anterior.

—Perdone, pero esta lista es de ayer —dije.

El afroamericano cerró los ojos por varios segundos tratando de recordar dónde había puesto la lista de hoy.

—«*I am so sorry*» —dijo en inglés. Hace unos minutos la tenía en la mano —dijo y revolvió una montaña de papeles como si jugara al dominó.

Encontró la lista debajo de un vaso vacío de *Starbucks*, doblada, y ya manchada con círculos de café. El anciano se ruborizó y pidió disculpas.

Firmamos y nos entregó una ficha con un número para pasar con el oficial. Fue el treinta y dos. Había que esperar. Nos sentamos en sillas de plástico verde y amarillo, como la bandera de Jamaica, y me recordaron los viajes en los camiones urbanos de Celaya.

No pasaron ni cinco minutos cuando el complaciente anciano, en inglés y con palabras sueltas en español, nos indicó que hiciéramos fila para entrar a la casilla número tres.

—Por favor «*make a line* y esperar *for the next official*» —dijo con una sonrisa. Compensaba su falta de español con su apabullante amabilidad.

Una pareja joven con sus hijos ya hacía fila. Tenían el número treinta y tres. Él estaba renegrido por el sol y flaco como cachorro con pulgas. Trabajaba pegando ladrillos en una empresa de italianos. Era el jefe de su cuadrilla y su cheque quincenal era la envidia del vecindario. Ella era una muchachita menuda y muy joven con apenas rastros de maquillaje. Su tez era blanca y tenía los dientes parejos y encendidas las mejillas; relumbraba de sana, parecía de Guadalajara. Les hablaba a sus hijos y al esposo con suavidad y firmeza como si fuera maestra de primaria o la presidenta de la Junta de padres de familia. La pareja se miraba desigual; como la niebla londinense y el sol acapulqueño. El Yin y el Yang del dualismo chino.

El hombre cargaba en sus brazos a una niña de ocho años como si fuera un bulto de cemento. No se encorvaba ni buscaba una pared para recargarse. Estaba altivo, estoico, firme, como si esperara una orden militar. Lucía sereno y exudaba confianza en sí mismo. De vez en cuando oteaba a la concurrencia y se sentía infinitamente superior. Pidió el día en su trabajo y lo disfrutaba. La niña se hacía la dormida y volvía a poner la cabeza en el hombro de su padre. La familia salió de su pueblo a las cuatro de la mañana. Llegaron a Madison justo media hora antes de su cita. El niño de en medio requería atención y le decía a su papá que la bajara que sólo se estaba haciendo la dormida. El papá no le hacía caso. Pensaba que tenía celos. El niño mayor, de catorce años cumplidos, seguía pegado con *Cola Loca* a la pantalla de su teléfono; ignoraba su entorno. Se perdía en el ciberespacio de Steve Jobs. Chateaba con Marisa, una niña de trece años. Aceptó a salir con él.

La señora, que yo pensaba era de Guadalajara, se salió de la fila y fue por segunda vez al baño. La gente que esperaba sentada, se le quedaba mirando con atención. Cuando regresó, le indicó a su esposo que el vestido que le dijo que se pusiera se le sube y se le levanta con los ventiladores. Ella quería venir de pantalón. De los que se expanden en la cintura. (El consulado no tenía aire acondicionado por orden de Manuel López Obrador; entró el plan austero). La señora jalisciense enseñaba una barriga de ocho meses; un balón oficial de basquetbol bailoteaba en su vientre. Razón por la cual, cuando respiraba y le llegaba la ráfaga de aire de los ventiladores, se le subía el vestido. Ya enseñó los muslos tres veces. El marido sonreía. No le importaba que la vieran. Pensaba que se sacó la lotería; su mujer era muy guapa; de tez clara, un cuerpo bien bien formado y cubierta por un velo de inocencia. El hombre ha trabajado como burro, y era feliz.

Su esposa le hablaba con dulzura. Se veía que lo quería mucho. Se bromeaban. Coqueteaban como si fueran novios recientes. La gente que esperaba sentada estaba como hipnotizada por la pareja y los miraba fijamente. Era una escena de la telenovela de las nueve de la mañana patrocinada por el Consulado de México. Era la única diversión en la sala de espera.

Una señora caribeña teñida de rubio y pintada como mona esperaba sentada su turno y le decía a su esposo de Zacatecas:

—Esa pareja no hace juego. Si yo fuera la mamá de la chica no hubiera permitido ese matrimonio.

—¡Mmm! —gruñó el esposo. El hombre, que parecía un soldado revolucionario de 1910 y que tenía las mejillas hundidas, secas y cuarteadas por los golpes del viento y del sol, no la miraba. No le hacía caso. Lleva años que no escucha a su mujer. Cuando se harta de su parloteo, se va a su jardín a cuidar sus matas de chiles verdes y sus jitomates.

—Ese hombre peludo y renegrido no la merece. Mira, le crece pelo hasta en la palma de la mano —dijo la caribeña con rabia.

—¡Y a ti qué! —rugió el zacatecano. El hombre lamentaba que su sombrero de palma no le cubriera las orejas para no escuchar las sandeces de su mujer.

—¡Tú también, no me mereces! —le espetó la caribeña con un gesto de soberbia—. Yo tenía un montón de pretendientes. En San Juan yo era la hija del doctor Bolaños Cela. Me iba a la playa y cuando me paseaba en el bikini rojo de tiritas se les caía la baba a los turistas. Aquí no soy nada. Sólo tu esposa, y bueno de eso..., ni para qué hablar.

—¡Bah! ¡Pues allá te hubieras quedado! —gritó el zacatecano. Pensó que esto de llevarla a su pueblo a pasar el invierno es un error garrafal.

La caribeña por su propia iniciativa iba a pedir la nacionalidad mexicana. Se mudaban a Zacatecas. La caribeña estaba harta del frío y de que la menospreciaran —limpia oficinas en un edificio en Cleveland—a Puerto Rico no se regresa porque les tiene pánico a los huracanes y lo que pasó con María es una indicación de la devastación que causan. El zacatecano pensó que haberse casado por arreglar los papeles fue un error mayúsculo. Con gusto le regresaría el anillo de bodas, le dejaría la casa y la cuenta conjunta del banco. La caribeña no come chile, detesta a Vicente Fernández, dice que el baile de la quebradita son puros brincos y que el zacatecano es tan callado como el fantasma de su abuelo.

La caribeña no paraba de hablar. Su hijo, de diecisiete años estaba allí también. La madre lo iba a hacer mexicano a la fuerza. Quiéralo o no. El muchacho no hablaba español. La mamá lo consentía, lo mimaba. El chico se dejaba querer. La mamá lo miraba fijamente de diferentes ángulos como si le estuviera haciendo una escultura. La madre no parpadeaba. Le alisaba el pelo, lo tomaba de la mano, le contaba chistes al oído. En un momento de la espera, le puso una mano en la nuca y le dio un beso en el cachete.

El muchacho llevaba aretes en las orejas y maquillaje en los ojos. El color era verde claro como ala de perico y resaltaba con la playera rosada. Los pantalones eran blancos y ajustados. Difíciles de ponerse. En el hombro llevaba un tatuaje; era un corazón que destilaba diminutas gotas de sangre. Había una inscripción que decía: «I love you, Frankie».

Llegamos al final de la fila y era el turno de mi prima Marta Fidela. La oficial del consulado, una veracruzana de rizos negros y de menos de treinta años nos pidió los papeles. Tenía los labios gruesos y pintados en forma de corazón. Vestía una camiseta negra de algodón fino de Perú y unos pantalones Calvin Klein de mezclilla ajustados y rotos en el muslo y la rodilla. Era viernes social. Sus ojos eran grandes y verdes. Casi no pestañeaba. Cuando la miré directamente se sonrojó y desvió la mirada. No llevaba anillo de casada. Hacía poco que se había separado del marido. Está en proceso del divorcio y lo va a dejar en la calle. Su abogado se llama Joseph Cohen y es el benefactor número uno de las mujeres indefensas.

—¿Es usted Marta Fidela Buenrostro Centeno? —preguntó la veracruzana.

—Sí señorita, para servir a Dios y a usted —dijo mi prima. La Veracruzana pensó que había leído esa frase en un libro de Elena Poniatowska que se llama: «Hasta no verte Jesús mío». A la chica le gusta leer, especialmente en el invierno cuando no asoma ni las narices a la calle. Entre el clima de Veracruz y el de Michigan hay un espacio infinito. Son como dos universos paralelos.

—Permítame su pasaporte vencido señora Marta Fidela. ¿Sigue viviendo en la misma dirección?

—No, señorita. Compramos un ranchito fuera de la ciudad. No es nada, pero ahí tiene su casa. Esa es la nueva dirección.

—Gracias. ¿Trajo las fotos?

—Sí, aquí las tiene. No salí bien, pero mi tío Juan decía «en las fotos salimos como somos».

—Bueno... por favor asegúrese que toda la información en esta forma es correcta. Su esposo la puede ayudar.

—No soy su esposo, soy su primo —aclaré al instante. No me gustan los malentendidos.

—¡Vaya! Pues se ha portado muy amable en traerla y ayudarla. ¿Es usted siempre así de amable? —preguntó y se tomó un rizo de su pelo y lo puso a girar en su dedo índice.

—¡Uff! Ni se imagina. Mi amabilidad no tiene límites —sonreí como un viejo lobo de mar a la vista de Caperucita Roja perdida en el bosque.

—Pues... ojalá nos visite más seguido. ¿Usted no necesita renovar su pasaporte, su visa, cartilla militar, carta poder o preparar un menaje a México?

—No, pero puedo ocupar todos esos servicios, aunque no me hagan falta —dije y mis dientes caninos filosos como dagas se sumaron a mi sonrisa.

—Dígame señora Marta Fidela, ¿por cuántos años desea el pasaporte? —dijo la veracruzana con una voz dulce y maternal.

—Pues... por tres años. ¡Quién sabe cuánto tiempo más me quede de vida! Y la verdad no tiene caso gastar más dinero.

—Yo le sugiero que lo haga por diez. Le daremos el cincuenta por ciento de descuento y la quiero ver aquí otra vez para la renovación de otros diez años. ¿Ya se hizo ciudadana americana? —preguntó.

—¡Dios me libre señorita! Yo amo a mi país —respondió con un sobresalto como si le hubieran pinchado el brazo con un alfiler.

—El hacerse ciudadana no le quita nada. Al contrario, le da más beneficios y necesitamos sacar al "Loco de la Casa Blanca."

—Tiene razón. Ya verá que seguiré su consejo.

—¿Algo más en que pueda servirles? Estoy a sus órdenes para lo que necesiten. Por favor siéntense y esperen. En unos minutos le darán su pasaporte nuevo.

—Gracias mil —dijimos al unísono mi prima y yo.

La veracruzana llamó ahora a la familia joven que hacía fila. Les iban a tomar la foto. Al instante, la niña que pretendía estar dormida bostezó y se alisó el pelo con los dedos. Se puso en pose y miró a la mamá. Las dos eran idénticas. Se sentía guapa y sonría.

Todos sus papeles estaban en orden. En media hora les darían los pasaportes. Iban a Puerto Vallarta de vacaciones.

Ya eran las cuatro y el lugar estaba casi vacío. Muchas personas arreglaron sus asuntos el mismo día, otros tendrían que regresar con los papeles que les faltaron. Los burócratas del consulado sintieron que cumplieron con su trabajo, se esforzaron por ser amables. Estaban satisfechos de ayudar a su gente. Más tarde se organizaron para irse a tomar una copa a "El Tapatío," un bar popular en el *Mexican Village*.

Mi prima por su parte estaba contenta. Feliz. Radiante. Fue un día rotundo; consiguió su pasaporte, salió guapa en la foto, le dieron descuento, le auguraron muchos años de vida y se evitó morir asfixiada en la cajuela de un carro.

—Te va a salir cara mi ayuda prima; tienes que comprarme el pasaje a la Riviera Maya, el traje para la boda, un traje de baño y ropa para pasear por la playa —dije.

—No te preocupes primo. Me gasto el dinero que le iba dejar al Juliancito de herencia. Al fin que no ayudó en nada —dijo Marta Fidela.

—Si tengo suerte, me consigo a una viuda pensionada de esas que caminan solas por la playa, de las que suspiran con los atardeceres, de las que beben Margaritas y checan diariamente la bolsa de valores y sonríen al ver su cuenta del banco —dije.

—O puedes visitar el Consulado de México en Madison cada semana, estoy segura de que te encantará el café veracruzano y los ojos verdes de la chica —la prima Marta Fidela Buenrostro Centeno dijo y se rió estrepitosamente.

Afuera, dos empleadas del consulado estaban subidas a la azotea del edificio; la bandera de México estaba siendo reemplazada por una nueva. La compró el cónsul de su propio dinero. Su mujer no estaba de acuerdo. Ella quería un traje de baño nuevo para estrenarlo en Manzanillo.

—Deja que López Obrador pague la bandera. Él sí tiene dinero. Y ahora más con todo lo que se va a robar con la construcción del Tren Maya —dijo la mujer del cónsul de mal humor.

El águila, bordada con hilos de oro en la bandera, luce altiva, orgullosa, bella. Las empleadas antes de bajarse se llevaron la mano al pecho y saludaron la bandera. Se quedaron unos minutos en silencio. La brisa ondeaba la bandera. Los colores verde, blanco y rojo restallaban contra el azul del cielo.

Eran las cinco de la tarde, los oficiales del consulado cerraron la puerta, apagaron las luces, bajaron las persianas y salieron presurosos, exultantes. Se distribuyeron en tres carros. Se iban de copas. Era viernes social y ya desde el estacionamiento había comenzado la fiesta.

11

Passport, or Death

When I put my brother-in-law in the trunk of my car, I didn't know if he would survive the trip. Death by asphyxiation is the most common, although dehydration and carbon monoxide poisoning are also deadly. The journey in the trunk of a car would be long and dangerous. We wouldn't stop until Saltillo, where the last checkpoint was located. If he survived, he would be the first German to enter Mexico illegally.

This was our vacation voyage to Mexico, and since our family is so large, we decided to make the trip by car. Multiple cars.

The story began when we arrived in Laredo, Texas, the section of the border we needed to cross if we wanted to continue on federal road 85D to the interior of Mexico. Upon trying to cross the customs gate of Nuevo Laredo Tamaulipas, the official on rotation didn't want to accept my brother-in-law's passport. Instead, they asked him to get out of the car and put him in a tiny, windowless room that smelled of cigarette smoke, disinfectant, and three-day-old food scraps. There were empty beer cans tossed in one corner and a mousetrap, no cheese.

The customs officials read his passport meticulously, reviewing each entry and exit of the countries he had visited. They examined the stamps with a magnifying glass. They inspected the age and type of ink used in the signatures. They interrogated him like he was an active member of Al-Qaeda or the Taliban. At the end of the investigation, the official on duty said: "This passport is fake. Here it says that you are a German citizen and you seem Hispanic; your physical characteristics are from the

Ixhuatán, Oaxaca region that borders Chiapas. Moreover, the photo is not you. This passport belongs to a much younger person."

"This passport is completely legal. I was born in Frankfort on May 18, 1950. Here is my U.S. green card. I don't know what the problem is," said my brother-in-law with a gesture of disgust.

"The thing is, you cannot come to Mexico with this fake passport. Now, if you want to visit this country well...we can arrange it."

"Arrange what? There's nothing to arrange. My passport is in order."

"Look, Sir, don't waste my time. If you're not going to play ball, I suggest you return to where you came from."

"I will not play ball or anything with you or anyone. I'd rather not go on vacation."

Obviously, Tiburcio Sánchez López, third generation in the lucrative extortion business, wanted his *mordida*.

At four in the afternoon, tired and baking in the miserable Laredo sun, my brother-in-law, the German with "Benito Juarez" traits, decided that he was not going to give up anything. I asked. I begged, I pleaded that he give a little something to the official, but he refused.

"It's a matter of principles," he said. "I was born in Germany, and there they don't do these things."

"Well...here they do. Here you can change your principles in an instant. In the morning, you have some, and at night you have others. The *mordida* is the oil that greases the wheel. Even presidents do it. It's tradition. Since colonial times. The Spaniards brought chickenpox and *la mordida*."

"No way! I'm not giving a cent to that rat. My papers are in order," said my brother-in-law, unhinged with rage.

We waited until nightfall, and at 11:30pm, I put my brother-in-law in the trunk of my car. I gave him a pillow, I covered him with a blanket, and I gave him a bottle of water. My wife, crying and frantic, blessed her brother with the sign of the cross. This could be the last time she saw him alive.

I read the panic on his face when I closed the lid of the trunk. My brother-in-law felt like we were closing the lid of a coffin on him. A passionate follower of Mexican cinema, he knew about Mexican jails, and of course, he did not want any reason to visit them.

Tiburcio Sánchez López, the first-shift customs official, had already gone. For him, it had been a slow Monday, and the fishing hadn't been good. A whole day and he had only extorted $223.43. Filomeno Gómez Farías—on the night shift—was his replacement, suffering a hangover that had his brain paralyzed and his muscles atrophied. More asleep than awake, he didn't want to interrupt his recovery and, with one hand, without even getting up from his comfortable position, gave us the signal to go ahead. No interrogation. No extortion. No passport. Nothing. At least we cleared the border bridge.

When we arrived in Saltillo, we had already passed all of the checkpoints. I stopped at The Sleeping Bear, a gritty motel—$15 per hour—to see how the German was doing. But no, there he was, serene as an angel and snoring like a drunk politician. Sound asleep, hugging the spare tire. He was golden. He passed the checkpoints with his eyes closed like a newborn puppy. I'd like to know if he's the first German citizen who sneaked undocumented into Mexico.

Finally, we woke him up and he said: "I'm pretty sore, but at least I didn't pay the bribe. Corruption stops with me. Today is an historic day! This country has to change already. When will that happen?"

"Well, when Jesus comes to raise the dead, we have a chance," I said.

When I told my cousin this 100% true story, her skin crawled, her pupils dilated, and drops of cold sweat ran down her spine. She went pale. Her blood pressure rose to 180, and she almost fainted.

Marta Fidela Buenrostro Centeno is a distant cousin, so remote that we rarely talk. Marta Fidela's youngest son, Juliancito, was getting married in the Riviera Maya, in a wedding on the beach at a five-star hotel. The ceremony would take place in five days, and her passport—this is the tragedy—had expired.

"What am I going to do? I want to die. I'll miss my son's wedding," she said and began to cry.

Juliancito, 43 years old, didn't want to get married; he was a bit lazy, and to prove it, he neglected his duties helping his fiancée organize the wedding. Ultimately the fiancée—who didn't give a damn—relegated all the work to her future mother-in-law. Marta Fidela, who wanted Juliancito to leave home so she could rent his room and sell his baseball card collection, decided to shoulder the responsibility of the wedding arrangements by herself.

She reserved the hotel for eighty-nine people, all of the rooms with an ocean view at the guests' insistence. She found a Catholic priest—which, in itself, is an epic act since most are in jail—at the Riviera Maya. She designed the menu including vegetarians and vegans, booked the mariachis, who smelled U.S. dollars and demanded $30 per song, ordered the roses from Colombia with extra import duties, ordered the *tres leches* cake and Victorian dresses for the bridesmaids.

Marta Fidela took charge of the wedding's most minute details that absorbed her in such a way that the last thing she thought about was checking to see if her passport was still valid. Rapt with panic and overcome with emotion, she called the Mexican Consulate in Detroit and begged, cried, threatened, and ultimately offered money. Even then, they told her that there were no appointments available to renew her passport.

"We are sorry. We couldn't make an exception even if Pope Francis was coming to marry your son. No exceptions; this is the new policy. You need an appointment to renew your passport, and there are no appointments until next month. Therefore, pray hard and see if anyone cancels," the official said.

"I'm tired of praying. I have no more saints to ask for help; I've burned through them all, and the truth is I'm at the point of losing faith."

From the point of view of my cousin Marta Fidela Buenrostro Centeno, who has constantly denigrated me and treated me like a pariah, two options remained:

Option one: stay where she is and watch the wedding on Zoom.

"How will Marta Fidela deal with not being able to go to the wedding just because she doesn't have a passport? She is 100% Mexican. She hasn't become a U.S. citizen because, for her, that seems like treason. So she's going to visit her country, her homeland," said my neighbor Altagracia Revueltas Patiño, who did me the favor of staying over and has now awoken with red eyes and a lion's mane after sleeping for twelve hours.

"And how can she prove she's from Mexico? With her native features, she could be from any Central American country. Now, with the 'migrant caravan' for sure, Immigration would deport her to El Salvador, Honduras, Nicaragua, or Guatemala. And the truth is, no offense, but that would be worse," she said.

"And what is the other option?" asked my neighbor, Altagracia, while picking up her underwear strewn all over the floor.

"The other option is to hide her in the trunk of a car and cross the border, arrive in Monterrey, and then take a plane to Riviera Maya. I'd do the same with her as I did with my brother-in-law, the German a few years ago," I said jokingly.

"Yes, that sounds good. The problem is that your cousin is already seventy-five years old. She suffers from anxiety, rheumatism, diabetes. She has only half a kidney, high blood pressure, and an accelerated heart rate," my neighbor said, who began to make the bed. I saw her placing her pajamas under the pillow as if she would stay some more days here.

"Well...if Marta Fidela survives the trip through the last checkpoint, then she can attend her son's wedding. If not, then the wedding will be suspended, and the funeral arranged. But, no matter what, the family would be together," I said with a sarcastic smile.

But then my cousin received a call from the Mexican Consulate in Detroit, and they told her that someone had canceled: "There is an opening for your appointment," said the official. "So which saint do you have to thank?"

"You won't believe it, but the *Santo Niño de Atocha* came through," she said.

Marta Fidela jumped with joy and offered to make a pilgrimage to *Santo Niño de Atocha* on her knees, dance barefoot all night in the atrium of the chapel—as tradition calls for when a miracle is performed—and fill his chapel with flowers.

Immediately, Marta Fidela called me and asked if I could please take her to Detroit to complete the passport process.

"Cousin, you have to take me to Detroit. I must renew my passport. Otherwise, I can't go to Juliancito's wedding."

"And your husband? Why doesn't he take you?"

"He can't see anymore. He doesn't drive. After the stroke, he became paralyzed on the right side. Only his left side works."

"And your children?"

"They are all gone. They moved up their vacations. My husband and I are the only ones still here. We had to take care of Grandma."

"I wasn't even invited to the wedding," I said reproachfully.

"We didn't tell you because we thought that since you are unemployed, you won't have the money to go. Also, you just got out of jail. So you need to enjoy your family, and you can't leave the country."

"That's my problem! But, anyway, you should have told me. And I can go anywhere I want!"

"Look Carlitos, now is not the time to read me the riot act. Help me, and I'll pay your airfare to Riviera Maya. I'm desperate. Only you can save me."

"Well, I'm not doing it for the trip. I'm doing it for you. And so that you learn not to reject those of us who have been through setbacks."

"Stabbing some guy was a setback?"

"Please, cousin, don't mess with me. I served my time. And anyway, it was just a scratch. It was self-defense."

The trip to Detroit was unpleasant, a city in ruins and practically abandoned. Ford, General Motors, Chrysler, and other automobile companies partially left, and the city went downhill. Downtown was littered with abandoned buildings, crumbling storefronts, restaurants with their lights off and broken windows, and a swarm of beggars and thieves who scoured the main square looking for victims.

"It looks like Chernobyl after the nuclear accident," my cousin said.

"And how do you know about Chernobyl?"

"I saw it on TV. In an HBO series," she said, and added, "Detroit is the same."

"Yes, the difference is that in Detroit the remaining inhabitants don't speak Russian and haven't been killed by radiation."

Due to the urban devastation of Detroit, the Mexican government—always looking to protect its citizens—moved its offices to Madison, a suburb of the city. Madison was a little town of orderly homes with gardens crammed with flowers, white painted fences, well-cut lawns, and children coming and going on bicycles.

The Mexican Consul, Mr. Rufino Rivera Fuentes, a relic of ancient times, rented a building in what was once an abandoned daycare center, and Mexican bureaucrats—always active—set it up as government offices. They removed the Mickey Mouse poster and replaced it with the portrait of the Mexican president Manuel López Obrador, took down Goofy, Donald Duck, and Elmo, and substituted them with paintings of Mexican heroes; Miguel Hidalgo, José María Morelos, and Agustín de Iturbide. The children's daycare center furniture was sold at the flea market, and with the earnings, they went to a place that sells office furniture second-hand. The Mexican Consulate was ready to serve the Mexican community in the northeast region.

We arrived at the address indicated by the navigator: 1403 East Twelve Mile Road, Madison Heights, Michigan, 48071. The Apple Maps Navigator assured us that this was the location of the Mexican Consulate, but it was a shopping center with restaurants and department stores. Furthermore, the consulate building could not be seen anywhere.

"There's no consulate here," I said.

"Keep looking, cousin. Maybe it's behind Walmart or Costco," said my anxious and desperate cousin.

We searched for half an hour, until we saw a sign drawn in crayons of different colors that announced that the Mexican Consulate could be found next to Pizza Hut and behind Burger King. I saw the building and thought it was a joke. Then, suddenly, a Mexican flag with the colors faded, and the eagle frayed—there was no money for a new one—indicated that this was, indeed the new Mexican Consulate. Our national representatives abroad had their offices in an abandoned children's daycare center.

We got out of the car and went toward the main entrance. On the door a sign said,"This door has no handle. Use the other door on the left."

We entered the waiting room, and it seemed like the lobby of an improvised cinema. I counted twenty-four rows of plastic chairs in different colors lined up before a digital screen. In five-window sections, like the tellers in a bank, you could see the officials. They were dressed in T-shirts and jeans; it was casual Friday. They stood ready to assist the people.

Immediately at the entrance, an elderly African American man with his front teeth missing greeted us. He had a several weeks-old beard and a black suit, frayed like he was a funeral director who had been caught in a dust storm in the plains of Texcoco. I thought he was a homeless man, a beggar seeking refuge from the heat in the Mexican Consulate. But no, he was an employee of the Mexican government, the attentive aide who greeted the visitors. The old fellow—compensating for his attire—was solicitous and obliging like an aide to a U.S. senator.

The man suffered the first symptoms of Parkinson's disease and, with a slight tremor of his right hand, offered us a paper with the names of the people who had appointments. Unfortunately, I couldn't find my cousin's name on the list. Instantly, I realized the list was for the previous day.

"Excuse me, but this list is for yesterday," I said.

The African American man closed his eyes for several seconds, trying to remember where he had put today's list.

"I am so sorry. I had it in my hands just a few minutes ago," he said and shuffled a pile of papers as if playing dominos.

He found the list under an empty Starbucks cup, folded and already covered in coffee rings. The man blushed and apologized.

We signed, and he gave us a numbered token to give to the official. It was thirty-two. We had to wait. We sat on green and yellow plastic chairs, like the colors of the Jamaican flag.

Not even five minutes had passed when the nice eighty-year-old man, in English with a few Spanish words thrown in, told us to line up at window number three.

"*Por favor* make a line and *esperar* for the next official," he said with a smile. He compensated for his lack of Spanish with overwhelming kindness.

A young couple with children was already in line. They were number thirty-three. The husband was sunburned and as thin as a puppy with fleas. He worked laying bricks for a company owned by Italians. He was the shift boss, and his bi-weekly check was the envy of the neighborhood. His wife was a petite and very young woman with hardly any trace of makeup. She had fair skin with even teeth and rosy cheeks, exuding good health; she seemed from Guadalajara. She spoke to her husband and children with gentle firmness as if she were an elementary school teacher or the PTA president. The couple looked mismatched, like the London fog and Acapulco sun. The Yin and Yang of Chinese dualism.

The man held an eight year-old girl in his arms like a bag of cement. He didn't stoop over or look for a wall to lean on. He was strong, stoic, determined as if waiting for a military order. He seemed unemotional and exuded confidence in himself. Occasionally, he glanced around the room and felt infinitely superior. He took the day off today, and he was enjoying it. His daughter was sleeping and nestled her head on his shoulder. The family left their town at four in the morning. They arrived in Madison half an hour before their appointment. The middle child wanted attention and told his father to put his sister down because she was only pretending to sleep. The father ignored him. He thought that he's just jealous. About fifteen years old, the eldest child was stuck to his phone screen, oblivious to his surroundings. He was lost in Steve Jobs' cyberspace. He was messaging Marisa, a thirteen year-old girl. She agreed to go out with him.

The young wife, who I thought was from Guadalajara, left the line and went to the bathroom for the second time. The people who were seated, waiting, looked at her attentively. When she returned, she indicated to her husband that the fans were blowing up and down the dress he told her to wear. She had wanted to wear pants with an elastic waist. The Consulate didn't have air conditioning per orders from Manuel López Obrador, due to austerity measures. The lady from Guadalajara showed her eight months belly; a regulation basketball danced inside. That was why when she breathed, the air from the fan lifted her dress. She already showed her thighs three times. The husband smiled. He didn't care who saw her. He thought he won the lottery; his wife was beautiful with fair skin and a lovely body; an air of innocence surrounded her. The man worked like a dog, but was happy. His wife spoke to him sweetly. She loved him. They joked around, flirted like newlyweds. The people who were seated waiting were practically hypnotized by the couple and stared at them intensely. It was the 9am Mexican soap opera, sponsored by the Mexican Consulate. This episode of real life was first-class entertainment.

A dyed-blond Caribbean woman sat and waited for her turn; she said to her husband, from Zacatecas:

"That couple doesn't match. If I were the mother of that girl, I would not have permitted that marriage."

"Mmm," growled her husband. The man, who looked like one of Pancho Villa's revolutionary men whose cheeks were dried and cracked from the wind and the sun, didn't look at her. He paid her no attention. He hadn't listened to his wife for years. When he tired of her rant, he went to the garden to take care of his green chili plants and tomatoes.

"That hairy and sunburned man doesn't deserve her. Look, he even has hair on the palms of his hands," said the Caribbean woman angrily.

"And what does it matter to you!" the Zacatecan man roared. The man lamented that his straw hat didn't cover his ears, so he couldn't hear his woman's nonsense.

"You don't deserve me, either!" snapped the Caribbean woman with a gesture of arrogance. "I had a ton of suitors. In San Juan, I was the daughter of Dr. Bolaños Cela. I'd go to the beach, and when they walked by me in my skimpy red bikini, the tourists would drool. Here, I am nothing. I'm your wife, and about that, well... there's no need to speak."

"Ahh! Well then, you should have stayed there," the Zacatecan man grumbled. He thought that taking her to his hometown for the winter was a monumental error.

The Caribbean woman, at her initiative, was requesting Mexican nationality. They were moving to Zacatecas. The Caribbean woman was tired of the cold and being unappreciated—she cleaned offices in a building in Cleveland—and she wouldn't return to Puerto Rico because hurricanes make her panic and what happened with María is an indication of the devastation they cause. The Zacatecan man thought that having married her for papers was a colossal mistake. He would have gladly returned the green card, the wedding ring, the house, and the bank account. The Caribbean woman didn't eat chiles jalapeños or any other kind of chiles, hated Vicente Fernández, said that dancing *la quebradita* is just hopping around like grasshoppers, and complained that her husband never talks and is as silent as her grandfather's ghost.

The Caribbean woman didn't stop talking. Her sixteen-year-old son was also there. She would make him Mexican by force whether he wanted it or not. He didn't speak Spanish. The mother adored him, pampered him; the boy let her. The mother looked at him intensely, from various angles, like she was making him in sculpture. She straightened his hair, took his hand, whispered jokes in his ear. She put a hand on the back of his neck and kissed his cheek.

The boy had earrings in his ears and eye makeup. The color was bright green like a parrot's wing and stood out against his pink shirt. His pants were skinny and white. They must have been difficult to put on. He had a tattoo on his shoulder: a heart dripping tiny droplets of blood. An inscription said,"I love you, Frankie."

The line moved forward, and finally, it was my cousin Marta Fidela's turn. The consular official, a woman under thirty from Veracruz, with black curls, asked us for the papers. She had plump lips painted in the shape of a heart. She was wearing a black shirt in fine Peruvian cotton and Calvin Klein jeans, tight, ripped at the thigh and knee. It was casual Friday. Her eyes were big and green. She barely blinked. When I looked at her directly, she blushed and looked away. She didn't have a wedding ring. She had separated from her husband a little bit ago. She was in the divorce process and was going to leave him out in the street. Her lawyer's name was Joseph Cohen, and he's the number one benefactor of defenseless women.

"Are you Señora Marta Fidela Buenrostro Centeno?" asked the Veracruzan woman.

"Yes, miss, here to serve God and you," my cousin said. The Veracruzan woman thought that she had read this phrase in one of Elena Poniatowska's books. The woman likes to read, especially in the winter when she doesn't even show her face outside. Between the climate of Veracruz and that of Michigan, there is an infinite abyss. They are like two opposite universes.

"Would you please hand me your expired passport? Do you still live at the same address?" asked the Veracruzan woman.

"No. We bought a little house outside of the city. It's not much, but we have our home there. Here is the new address."

"Thanks. Did you bring pictures?"

"Yes, here they are. I don't look great, but my grandfather used to say 'in pictures, we come out the way we are.'"

"Well... please make sure all the information on this form is correct. Your husband can help you."

"I'm not her husband. I'm her cousin," I clarified instantly. I don't like misunderstandings.

"Well... you've been very kind to bring her and help her. Are you always this kind?" she asked, taking a curl and winding it around her finger.

"Oh! You can't even imagine. My kindness knows no limits," I smiled like the Big Bad Wolf seeing Little Red Riding Hood lost in the woods.

"Hopefully, you will visit us more often. But, don't you need to renew your passport, visa, military ID, or prepare a homestead in Mexico?"

"No, but I can make use of all of those services, even though I don't need them," I said, my dagger-sharp canine teeth adding to my smile.

"Tell me, Señora, how many years do you want the passport to last?" asked the Veracruzan woman in a sweet and maternal voice.

"Well... for three years. Who knows how much time I have left? The truth is, there's no reason to spend more money."

"I suggest you make it for ten. We'll give you a 50% discount, and I want to see you here for the renewal in another ten years. Have you already become an American citizen?"

"Heaven help me! I love my country!" she responded with a jump, as if her arm had been pricked with a pin.

"Becoming a citizen doesn't take anything from you. On the contrary, it gives you more benefits, and we have to remove this Crazy Person from the White House."

"You are right. You'll see, I'll follow your advice."

"Is there anything more I can do for you? I'm here to help with anything you need. If there isn't anything else, please sit down and wait. In a few minutes, we will give you your new passport."

"Thank you so much," my cousin and I said in unison.

Then the Veracruzan woman called the young family waiting in line. They were going to have their photos taken. Instantly, the girl who pretended to be asleep yawned and combed her hair with her fingers. She struck a pose and looked at her mother. The two were identical. She felt pretty and smiled. All their papers were in order. In half an hour, they would get their passports. They were going on vacation to Puerto Vallarta.

It was 4pm, and the place was practically empty. Many people had gotten their business done on the same day, while others had to come back with the missing papers. The consulate officials felt like they did their jobs. They went out of their way to be polite; they felt satisfied for having helped the people. Later they would arrange to meet and have a drink at El Tapatío, a popular bar in Mexican Village.

My cousin, for her part, was satisfied, joyful. It was a full day: she got her passport, she looked pretty in the photo, they gave her a discount. Marta Fidela was promised many more years to live, and she avoided death by asphyxiation in the trunk of a car.

"This is going to cost you a ton, cousin; you have to buy my ticket to Riviera Maya, a suit for the wedding, a bathing suit, and clothes for the beach." I said.

"Don't you worry cousin. I will spend the money I was going to leave to Juliancito as his inheritance. He didn't help at all with this wedding. He is useless."

"If I'm lucky, I'll romance one of those wealthy widows walking alone on the beach. One of those who sigh with the sunsets, who drink margaritas and check the stock market every day, smiling at their bank account," I said.

"Or you can visit the Mexican Consulate in Madison every week. I'm sure you will love the Veracruzan coffee," cousin Marta Fidela Buenrostro Centeno laughed loudly.

Two ladies from the Consulate were up on the roof; the Mexican flag was being replaced with a new one. The Consul bought it with his own money. His wife disagreed. She wanted a new swimsuit.

"Let Lopez Obrador pay for it. He has a ton of money, not counting the money he is going to steal from the construction of the Mayan Train," said the Consul's wife with an angry face.

The gleaming, proud eagle in the emblem, embroidered with gold threads, avidly devoured the evil serpent. Before coming down, the ladies saluted the flag and placed their hands over their hearts. They remained in silence for a few minutes. The summer breeze waved the flag: the colors green, white, and red burst against the blue of the sky.

It was 5pm. The consular officials closed the door, turned off the lights, lowered the blinds and left hurriedly, happy. They broke away into three cars. They were going to have a drink. It was casual Friday and already, in the parking lot, the party had started.

The Nest

Eldis Rodriguez-Baez

Shari Nacson

Originally from New Jersey, I am a mother, clinical social worker, freelance editor, writer, and nonprofit consultant. My pro bono work centers around trauma, immigration justice, reproductive justice, criminal justice, and racial equity.

After serving as a grand jury foreperson in 2019, my passion for justice led me to co-found Citizens for Grand Jury Reform. In all my work, it is an honor to be trusted to help people speak their truths in the fight against oppressive policies, systems, and people.

12

Threads of Migration

We know how important it is, psychologically, to be oriented to time and space. Anyone who has relocated—short or long distances—knows that it takes a while to get your groove back, to do your normal things in a new place. Under the best of circumstances.

So, if a planned move is tricky on our best days, what about fleeing? A disorganized and fear-based departure undoes all human anchors. Untethered, to then embark on a crisis-based migration, hoping to be allowed safe harbor. Perseverance through prolonged uncertainty is fueled by hope. Day after day of walking, hunger, and fear. Accepting kindnesses, feeling pain and discomfort, longing for home—fueled by the hope that safe harbor lies at the end of the journey.

Only to be greeted by hostility, suspicion, rejection, and imprisonment? This betrayal compounds whatever hardship led to the flight from home and is exacerbated by the exhaustion, malnourishment, and cognitive fatigue of the physical task of migration.

We know that a large portion of those seeking refuge in the United States have migrated in this way. As an emergency. Requesting asylum at the border or passing through undetected—perhaps with a relative's address in hand, landing with kin.

We know that detention—originally meant to be a pause before receiving the go-ahead to stay while formally applying for asylum—has become prolonged and is entangled with our for-profit prison system. We know that, of those who cross the border illegally—where they once could get by with under-the-table wages while seeking legal residency and citizenship—now fear being picked up by ICE and placed in jail.

A portion of Ohio detainees are in this latter cohort. They have lived and worked here, raised children here, and are embedded in our communities. If they are picked-up by ICE, they often wind up in local jails (Geauga, Butler, Morrow, and Seneca Counties and Bedford Heights City at the time of this writing). Those picked-up at or near our southern border land in these jails or federal prisons.

One of things that has struck me the most, as I've observed immigration court hearings and visited jails to meet with ICE detainees, is the sheer volume of asylum seekers who did not intend to come to Ohio. They have won the lousiest of lotteries. The prize includes food of questionable quality, tan scrubs, a pair of Crocs, a plastic-covered name badge alligator-clipped to their shirt, and a trip to a state they have never even heard of.

ICE detainees get a different color of scrubs to distinguish them from the "'real' inmates. In our prison (Youngstown), ICE detainees get their own wing, where they have "more privileges and freedoms" than people there serving time for crimes. In other locations across the country and in Ohio, they mix ICE detainees with the general prison or jail population.

To visit a prison, professionals need to be authorized. I was told to dress conservatively. They do not allow cell phones. I bring a notebook, any papers that I need, a pencil, a business card, and my car keys. I trade my driver's license for a visitor's badge and put my belongings through the metal detector. Between prison visits and going to immigration court, I've learned to wear slip-on shoes and pants that don't require a belt—because I'm not keen on whisking-off and then re-threading my belt at security.

I am one of the clinicians in northern Ohio who go to the prisons and jails to conduct pro bono psychological evaluations of immigration detainees. Evaluations are requested by attorneys who feel it could help clarify things for the immigration judge who is considering the applicant's request for asylum. Evaluators meet with clients for several hours. Through interviews and the use of some standardized measures, we do a full psychological assessment that becomes a report to the judge.

A key part of that meeting with the client—often we are allowed only one opportunity to meet with people who are detained—is hearing their migration story. It is through these stories that I have come to understand how random the route becomes once crossing the southern border into the United States.

The route is intentional when people leave their home countries. They have a destination in mind as they trek for weeks by foot, by bus, by the kindness of strangers. They know they are not safe in their home country. They have left even though they wished to stay with their loved ones in the only home they have ever known. They believe that their story of the danger they fled is clear and that they will be met with compassion.

That does not happen. Those who present themselves at the border find themselves rejected (and therefore people like me have yet to meet them because they are forced to "remain staying in Mexico") or "detained"—which is, essentially, being arrested and put in jail. U.S. officials confiscate their property. Identity documents are often permanently lost in this process. People who are detained go into a holding facility as has been depicted in the news—cold, hard floors, Mylar blankets, no way to orient to time or space.

In that 72-hour hold, there is some administrative work to process these new arrivals. People—refugees—are tracked like inventory. Family and friend groups are separated and channeled to whichever contracted facilities are in the queue to receive another bus/plane load of people. One refugee told me they sometimes labelled them with brightly colored tags with city abbreviations on them—like airport luggage—so staff can easily sort detainees for routing.

When I ask for their stories, there is often confusion about where in the U.S. they have been. Texas, Arizona, California? Layovers at unknown airports. Herded onto planes and busses. Most do not know the precise states they stayed in. Sometimes their papers tell us. By the time I meet with them, they know they are in Youngstown. I assume this is because of talking with their peers in the ICE wing, prison staff, and attorneys. I doubt they had ever heard of Ohio—let alone Youngstown—before they left their home countries. I doubt they could locate their whereabouts on a map.

In addition, over the 72-hour holding period and relocation transfers to get to the destination jail, there is more English being spoken at the detainees. Physically and linguistically isolated—having taken a journey they didn't want to take in the first place, but did because it was life-saving—detained asylum seekers lose the anchor of the outdoors. One gentleman told me about his months at the Geauga County Jail, which had no provision for time outside. He went months without daylight.

In the prison setting, despite having "more privileges" in the ICE wing, the outside is time-limited and fenced-in—with coils of concertina wire at the top. Hearing about people's home countries—where many worked out-of-doors most days—the industrial prison setting is truly alien.

It is exponentially demoralizing.

If people who are detained can access funds to buy an overpriced calling card, their friends or family at home or in the States will learn about Youngstown. Maybe they will look it up on the internet and have a sense that we are far from Florida, Texas, and California, but not really near New York City. They will hear about snow and wind. Geese on the grass inside the fences. Strange foods. New friends from other countries who are also detained. Lawyers and helpers who will or won't "take the case." "A numbers" and commissary accounts. Prayers and Bible study. Prison jobs to pass the time.

The luckiest ones are those who can "bond out." When this happens (which is by no means a simple or frequent thing), these asylum seekers are released from jail to stay with a designated U.S. citizen or permanent resident. Their personal items are somehow returned to them—having made the journey from the border crossing to the holding facility to the busses and planes. I should say that some personal items have migrated—the clothes. Far too often, important papers and identity documents have disappeared.

I think about these clothes a lot. Clothes worn trekking across tropical zones to our southern border. Clothes not seen for months and months, the wearer having gotten used to the tan scrubs and the Crocs—maybe having been fortunate enough to have someone wire money for price-gouged sneakers that are not allowed to leave the prison. Time-capsuled clothes. A bizarre consolation prize of familiar threads returned after profound betrayal and indignities. I wonder if these clothes are amulets. The only thing besides body and mind that has made the entire journey. Yet, the clothes were not part of the prison experience. Is that a kindness? To have one small thing spared? Or was the separation from these threads of migration another layer of loss and indignity?

Untethered. Perpetually disoriented by systems and institutions. By the grace of human kindness, hopefully greeted at the bus station by volunteers who provide warm clothes and guidance on how to navigate the next part of this migration journey. Possibly staying in Ohio because strangers have stepped-up to function as kin. Possibly traveling by bus or by plane to more places unknown, until finally landing with family or friends.

None of it the way they originally imagined it when leaving home.

All of it hard and unfair, yet encapsulated in gratitude for being still alive.

Alive.

Far from home.

By way of Youngstown.

Katie Salupo

Katie Salupo is from Youngstown, Ohio. She is a graduate of John Carroll University and a former elementary teacher. Katie is a wife and mother of three. She currently runs a small business.

Since the Youngstown "Bus Station Project" ended in 2020 with the closure of the ICE prison, Katie volunteers her time as the Housing Coordinator for Full Spectrum Community Outreach, raising funds to open Youngstown's first LGBTQ+ homeless shelter.

13

Why Do You Do This?

I started a project that helps migrant men right after they are released from the ICE prison in Youngstown, Ohio. We like to call ourselves an organized disorganization. We do not have meetings, a bank account, or foundation grants. We are simply a group of people who saw a need and stepped up to help. We rarely publicize our work because the men we serve—who we call "friends"—are sometimes dropped off at the bus station a few hours before the ticket window opens or before our volunteers arrive. Left very vulnerable, we want to protect their privacy and safety.

Five nights a week, a volunteer goes down to the bus station to meet the immigrant men who have been released from the ICE prison in Youngstown, as their cases continue to work through the courts. The men are often dropped off at the station with nothing but their release papers and the clothes on their backs. Most of our newly released friends do not speak English, but are left to make arrangements for their bus tickets (which doesn't always go smoothly) and learn how to navigate a U.S. bus journey, which usually includes multiple layovers and transfers.

The men are traveling all over the country; some face up to a three-day bus ride to meet up with family or friends in all parts of the United States. Savvy with Google translator, our volunteers give them traveling bags with toiletries, snacks, a change of clothes, blankets and coats, hats and gloves in the winter, and money to get food along the way. We help them purchase their bus tickets and teach them how to read them.

We've gotten pretty good with our Google translator. And we allow them to use our phones to call their loved ones.

I could tell you these men's stories and talk to you for hours about conditions at the jail or how they've been treated by our government, but I promised to keep this short, so I'll give you some "highlights."

I have seen a grown man openly weep in the middle of the bus station when he saw his mother's face on FaceTime.

I have seen bullet wounds, as a new friend told me how he escaped from his home country.

I have heard about a young man's parents who sold all of their belongings, including their home, to send him to America, because he was going to be killed for refusing to join a gang.

I have seen men huddled together by a heat vent because they were released in Ohio in January, wearing only t-shirts.

I've been offered snacks from the bag I just gave a man, as he tells me the story of traveling for months to get to the U.S., sometimes going days without food.

I have seen countless looks of relief and smiles, and been given many hugs and homemade souvenirs and art work created while in prison.

I have been told I am the first person who was kind to them since they've been in our country.

I have been told by a young man with tears in his eyes that until I came to the station, he was so scared and didn't think he would ever get to his family.

I'm constantly asked by my new friends, "Why do you do this?" They always think it's part of my job. I've been asked if I'm a nun, a social worker, work for ICE, or work for the government. My answer every time is, "Because you are a human being and should be treated like a human being."

Through the Bus Station Project, I have met the most amazing people who have helped me believe in the goodness of humanity. Our project runs completely through donations and volunteers. I've had people give of their time and volunteer to go to the station regularly. I have had countless church groups and civic groups give generous donations and conduct drives for our supplies. A group of junior high students wrote and then translated "Welcome" cards to deliver to our friends. A youth group run by teenagers collected coats in their community for our friends at the bus station. I've had volunteers who were college students and volunteers who were retired couples.

I have learned that wanting to help our migrant friends transcends any religion. I have met with Unitarians, Catholics, Mennonites, and Presbyterians who have all come together to help our fellow man.

I was not searching for a volunteer opportunity, I stumbled upon this situation and was unable to pretend it wasn't happening or look away without doing something to help. This project and the people I have met have been my light during dark times.

Around the Globe

Eldis Rodriguez-Baez

Awa Harouna

Awa Harouna is the oldest daughter in a first-generation immigrant family from Mauritania. An aspiring nursing student and creative writer, her father's near-deportation was documented in the Netflix original series, *Living Undocumented* (Episode Six), during the year he was detained.

14

Speak, Daughter

I was my mother's daughter,
Long before I would become
My father's voice.

The women in my family
Carried a history of oppression
In the marrow of their bones.
Made too small by the hands of men,
Made too rough by the ache
Of children born too early,
And years lost to toiling away
In search of better days.

The men in my family
Carried a history of subjugation
In their blood.
Skin too dark, hands too rough,
They were children that were forced
To grow too quickly, too mean.
When he was born, the world
Had looked at him and saw
Something small and gentle
And took from him what it could,
What it wanted,

What it did not deserve.
He saw for himself what violence

Had wrought, seeing death
Before he would ever love.

How he survived it all,
I will never know.

When he met my mother,
I like to think that it healed him
Just enough — this love
That they had —
For his eyes to soften
And his hands unclench.

I was my mother's daughter
Down to the skin of my bones
Made hard by a history
I never witnessed, but still carried
Between clenched teeth
And sharp eyes.

But my words —
They had always belonged to him,
To my father.

I did not know it at the time,
That each word that left my mouth,
Be it spiteful,
Empowering or enlightening,
Had always been his —
— words he could never speak

In those days spent away
From his family, his home,
Never knowing what the next day
May bring.

I became my father's daughter
The same way I became my mother's —
— I carried a history of oppression
Never witnessed, never experienced
But burdened nonetheless.

My mother taught me
That in our blood there lived
A flame,
And iron,
A will to survive
Beyond any means.

And my father taught me
To speak for peace.

Mory Keita and Lynn Tramonte

Mory Keita came to the United States at the age of three. Originally from Guinea, he spent thirty years of his life in Ohio with his family. Keita was unjustly deported to Guinea on a charter plane in December 2020, following months of detainment in the Morrow and Butler County Jails.

Mory was a key witness in a civil lawsuit against Butler County Jail, outside of Cincinnati. The jail, which detained immigrants on behalf of Immigration and Customs Enforcement (ICE) while awaiting court decisions on their cases, was notorious for racist and physical abuse against people held there. Kieta agreed to testify on the inhumane treatment of the immigrants by the guards, but was deported to Guinea before he could do so. The lawsuit remains pending, but the Butler County Jail no longer has a contract with ICE.

Lynn Tramonte is the Director of the Ohio Immigrant Alliance and President of Anacaona, LLC, a communications consulting firm. Tramonte works with immigrants, family members, and allies to expose abuses in ICE detention, stop the deportation of beloved Ohioans, and call for policies that allow deported people to return home.

15

We Have Kids Too

Mory Keita was deported to Guinea in December 2020. He was a key witness in a civil rights lawsuit against the Butler County Jail, where guards had repeatedly beaten men detained for ICE, called them monkeys, and told them to go back to Africa. Bayong Brown Bayong and Ahmed Adem bravely spoke out about this violence, and lawyers helped them file a lawsuit.

It's hard to overstate the courage it took for Bayong, Ahmed, and Mory to speak up, knowing that their very ability to remain in the U.S. was in jeopardy, along with their physical safety inside the jail's walls. Still, these men have rights. They knew it. And they have people on the outside helping them enforce their rights.

Being in the U.S. without a visa is a civil violation, but the law still allows people to be detained in regular jails. It does not require them to be detained. I've gotten to know many people held in jails for ICE over the years and I can say, without any doubt, that the practice is inhumane and must be ended. It's coercive, cruel, and mentally and financially exhausting. It affects children and entire families, and the logistics of detention make it harder for immigrants to get lawyers and build a strong legal case.

The system works as designed, not as we were taught in American Government class (where civil and human rights were supposed to be protected by the Constitution). The only "point" immigration detention serves is to break people's spirits so they give up and agree to be deported.

But Mory grew up here. He was a toddler when he came to the United States. And he has no family in Guinea; Ohio is the only home he ever knew.

Heroic lawyers C.K. Wang and Nazly Mamedova filed an emergency writ in federal court just hours before Mory was to be deported, trying to stop ICE from carrying out this injustice. A federal judge ordered ICE to keep him in the U.S. to provide testimony for the civil rights suit. But the plane was already in motion and ICE refused to comply.

I spoke with Mory over the phone in Guinea, a couple days after his deportation, and took this testimony. He agreed to share it with the public because he knows that what happened to him was wrong.

— Lynn Tramonte

Cleveland Heights, Ohio

Interview With Mory Keita After His Deportation (Rough Transcript)

Recorded: 12/17/20, 1:30pm ET

Participants: Mory Keita (MK), Lynn Tramonte (LT)

LT: State your name and location.

MK: My name is Mory Keita and I'm in Guinea, Conakry.

LT: When you were transferred from immigration detention in Ohio to Alexandria, LA, were you ever shown a travel document that pertains to you?

MK: No. I kept asking them. Every time I asked, they said they had my travel documents, and they never showed me a travel document. Only time they showed me a travel document it was not even a document, it was just some papers and stuff with the Guinea flag colors around it and my name was written in with an ink pen so I asked my deportation officer, how did you get my travel document? I never spoke to the embassy. Everybody who had a document before, they had an interview with the embassy.

I was wondering how they got the travel document and they never showed it to me like the actual paper. And they came and picked me up from Butler County and took me to Louisiana, and when I got there, I was still asking them where my travel document was. They never provided a travel document to me. The last time an ICE guy came in and I asked him, he said he was going to mail it to my lawyer, and I never saw a travel document.

LT: Did you ever request to speak to your embassy while you were in immigration detention?

MK: Yes, I did. I asked them over and over; I asked them over ten times and they said no, they can't do anything, I'm the one who needs to contact my embassy. And because of COVID stuff, all the embassies were closed and every time I called from detention I didn't get through. Every time I asked them they didn't want to provide anything, they just kept me running around and I know they didn't have my travel document.

LT: Do you have a birth certificate or have you ever seen one that belongs to you?

MK: No, I've never seen anything like that. When they came to see me when I was in Morrow County [Correctional Facility, another ICE detention center in Ohio] the lady, she came over there and told me they had my travel document in 2018 and they had my birth certificate. And I had never seen my birth certificate, so I was looking forward to seeing my birth certificate so I could get my stuff together. I never saw it.

LT: Now in Guinea, do you have documentation that proves who you are?

MK: No, I don't. When we got to Guinea yesterday, it was a little dark, and we got pulled over. There were a bunch of teenagers with guns, and they were asking for everybody's papers. I didn't have a document; I tried to tell them, but they had guns and I was frightened. They were speaking in French; I don't speak French. I was terrified about what they were going to do. My life passed what I went through before.

LT: Then what happened?

MK: The teenagers, when they stopped us, they kept asking a bunch of questions and they were going to take us somewhere but the guy I was with is a guy I got deported with, so he is the one who paid them a bunch of money, him and his family, so they could let us go.

LT: That happened last night?

MK: Yeah, last night. When they dropped me off. Because I didn't have any identification. I didn't have any type of papers to show them because I didn't have a travel document or a paper saying this is me right here, and this is my birthday, and this is where I'm from, I didn't have any of that.

LT: If they were teenagers, why were they asking for your ID?

MK: I don't know. I think they were just trying to kidnap us and get some money because they think that we just came from the United States and we have some kind of money.

LT: Did you get your travel document when you arrived at the airport in Guinea?

MK: No. I asked them when we got to Guinea, I asked the ICE agent where my travel document was. Y'all brought me all the way from Louisiana, twelve hours shackled in handcuffs, and can I get my travel document? He said he was going to give it to the military people; the ones working downstairs in the airport, the ones who came and picked us up. When I go downstairs, they almost put their hands on me because I didn't want to go downstairs without my travel document. I didn't want them to hurt me, so I just went and walked out. I asked the guy where the travel document was at; he said ICE never gave them anything. Only thing on paper they gave me was a paper saying transfer, that was it.

LT: Like an airplane ticket? Or what do you mean?

MK: No, it was like my medical papers and stuff. It was in a brown bag that said transfer on top.

LT: Did they give you that packet?

MK: Yes.

LT: What did you say about your case to ICE on the morning of your deportation?

MK: I asked them for my travel document and they came in a large group ready to beat on me then because I didn't want to come out of my cell without my document. They were talking about how if anybody doesn't want to go they are going to wrap you up in whatever surround stuff and put you on that plane.

LT: Did they physically force you out of the cell?

MK: I didn't want them to put their hands on me, because they came in like they will put their hands on us. Another ICE officer came over there like, do we have any problems today and one guy says yeah, only one person, that's all. I just went in like OK, I don't want them to beat me up, break my arm or my leg.

LT: Did you tell ICE anything about your case?

MK: Yes I said that the humanitarian people I have been talking to, you told me my lawyers filed my papers to the federal court, and I told them to look, can you look into your computer and see if my case is there if they are cancelling my order of removal. He said no, we checked everything, we got your travel document, we saw nothing. I said did you check the federal or ICE and he said oh I checked everything already, I don't want to go through this right here. When we get there, we will give your travel document to those people.

LT: At any point while you were on the plane, did anybody talk to you about the case?

MK: No, nobody did. I kept trying to talk to them at least before we left; I asked them like ten times, please Sir can you just check it for me because I know my lawyer filed it. I need to stay here because I'm going through stuff if I go back there. They still kept ignoring me, they didn't want to talk to me. The supervisor [unintelligible].

LT: So there was never any discussion about a judge's order or halting your deportation?

MK: No, they never talked about any of that to me.

LT: Did they have phones? Could they communicate on the ground?

MK: Yes, they had their phones. Every stop we made they had their cell phones, and they kept texting their people, talked to their girls, but they never once made a call for us.

LT: Now let's talk about the Butler County Jail lawsuit. Since you are one of the few people who witnessed both assaults on Bayong, your testimony is important. How will you be able to assist in the case from Guinea?

MK: I can't. Because there's a bunch of stuff going on here. There're protests and a bunch of stuff.

LT: Do you have a place to live?

MK: No. I stay with my brother I met from a long time ago, when I was younger. Thanks to him, we met up in Louisiana and that's the person I'm staying with now.

LT: So this is not a blood relative, but somebody you knew from a long time ago?

MK: No, it's not [a blood relative]. He's just, I don't even know how to thank him. I swear. Because if it wasn't for him, I wouldn't have known what to do. I would have been out there and I don't have anywhere to go. What about the guys who stopped me, they could take me and do whatever they want to do to me?

LT: What is happening in Guinea? Why do you think you are a target and why were you attacked last night?

MK: Because I just came from the United States and they think people have money and I have dreadlocks and stuff. They think I'm a criminal and I'm here without papers trying to do something to somebody; I don't know.

LT: How are you going to get papers in Guinea?

MK: I don't know. Without a document, if they would have given me my travel document, I would have had at least an ID or something.

LT: Is there anything else you'd like to say?

MK: I'm just a little scared right now because of how things are going, I don't know what to do. I'm just like, I'm feeling speechless right now because it's so corrupt how immigration treats people. They go beyond in doing stuff to people and they have no remorse. They deported fourteen people without their documents. A lot of guys I've seen over here, they have the same story I'm going through right now. It's ridiculous. I thought ICE was supposed to make sure we were OK. We are not criminals. I told them what was going on in Guinea, the protests and all kinds of crazy stuff going on. I told them I don't know anybody, if I go over there, what am I going to do? At least they could, like, feel for people, but they don't feel for people, they don't care. The only thing they care about is probably their check. Some of them have kids; we have kids too; you know? At least give me a fair trial, because I never received court date papers in the mail.

LT: When you were deported, did ICE give you any of the money that was on your books?

MK: *No, they didn't get me anything. They didn't even give me a penny. They didn't give me anything.*

The Immigrant
Eldis Rodriguez-Baez

Saidu Sow and Grace Goldstein

Saidu Sow was born in Nouakchott, Mauritania in 1977. He grew up with a love of soccer and the folkloric music of his Fulani people. Sow despised how the ruling class in his country oppressed Black people, and became involved in politics as a teenager.

After graduating from high school in 1997, he completed one year of a Computer Science program, but the Mauritanian government began targeting Sow due to his advocacy for human rights and equal treatment. He fled to the United States in 2001.

Now, Sow considers himself both a Mauritanian and American. While detained for U.S. Immigration and Customs Enforcement (ICE) for three years, he continued to expose abuses inside Ohio county jails at great personal risk. He was deported to Mauritania in July 2021.

Sow dreams of real freedom, seeing his daughter, and playing the guitar and soccer again.

Gracie Cahill Goldstein is a student at Kenyon College in Gambier, Ohio, where she plans to major in English. She's been published in *Seventeen Magazine*, *The Collegian Magazine*, *The Kenyon Collegian*, and *The Stuyvesant Spectator.* Goldstein works as a *Kenyon Review* Associate, critiquing weekly submissions to the renowned literary magazine. She grew up in New York City where she's been a community organizer, especially in the climate justice and gun control movements. She covers protests as a journalist when she is home.

16

I'm Alive

I was introduced to Saidu Sow by Lynn Tramonte in fall 2020. I was writing an article about ICE detention at Morrow County Jail for my college's newsmagazine and needed an interview with someone living on the inside, which seemed like a long shot when I first thought of it. By the time we got on the phone, Saidu had been moved from Morrow to the Butler County Jail. When he called me, I was nervous—I was a first-year college student asking an adult with overwhelming lived experience to tell me his personal story and talk about the greatest injustices of his life.

As soon as I asked my first question, I realized I did not have to worry so much about the interview—Saidu wanted to talk. He walked me through life as a refugee before and after 2017, ICE agents and corrections officers inside Morrow County Jail, politics and oppression in Mauritania, and everything else that mattered. We talked for half an hour, mostly him sharing stories, before the call was cut off as I thanked him.

I was frozen afterward, in a way that did not make sense, because I thought I already knew the extent of how dark and frustrating ICE detention is. I had read secondhand accounts in the news, and on activist websites, but having a conversation with someone stuck in the middle of it was a shock to the system.

Saidu lost his chance at asylum because a letter containing his court date got lost in the mail. That is a symptom of a system that is not exactly broken. It was not built to work. A dehumanizing system created an array of impossible situations for a vast population of completely normal, innocent people. It is too big a thing to capture verbally, and there are too many lived experiences to collect. But the more is said about the broken immigration system, directly from the mouths of people in detention, the better.

When I finalized my article, a long investigative story covering every aspect of the jail, I spent most of my time agonizing over which parts of our conversation to include. So much of what Saidu said was worth reporting. Everything felt explosive. But I couldn't print it all. I immediately hoped for an opportunity to give a more complete version of our conversation. Here are parts of our interview, transcribed and lightly edited for clarity by me.

—Grace Goldstein
Gambier, Ohio

Excerpts from Saidu Sow's Collegian Magazine Interview (Rough Transcript)

Recorded: 3/11/21
Participants: Saidu Sow (SS), Grace Goldstein (GG)

PART 1

GG: Hi, this is Gracie Goldstein... I really appreciate you talking to me. How are you right now?

SS: I'm alive.

GG: Yeah. Where are you right now? I think the automated voicemail said you're in Butler County. You're at Butler County Jail?

SS: Yes.

GG: How long were you in Morrow County Jail?

SS: Morrow County... a year?

GG: And how long have you been living in the US?

SS: Twenty years.

GG: So, if you're comfortable talking about it. What was your life like in the US? Before 2017. What was it like being an asylum seeker under the Obama administration, before things changed?

SS: Wow. It was a big difference. Very big difference. From the early 2000s to, actually, late 2016. Before the [Trump] administration got into office... America was different from the America that I saw the last four years. It was different. They don't... [say] "You're not one of us," and just mistreat you the way... discriminate [against] you because you're not American.

Because that is something I learned, in an ICE facility. But that is not something that I knew before, and I'll be telling people about it, that's a new thing to me. Because I never—don't get me wrong...being outside on the streets working, you might find one or two individuals who probably have a hate, or some way they look at things. But it was not open. They do it by hiding.

PART 2

SS: ICE officers are hostile. Sometimes racist. I mean I hate to use that word, because it's a strong word to use, but it is facts. And they discouraged me multiple times. And a lot of different people that I saw who don't even speak English, to even think about...trying to stay with their family in the United States. They will tell you you're wasting your time.

"When you go to court, well, you want to go to court? You can go to court. I'm gonna see you in a year, and after that, I will deport you." They will tell you directly.

When I came here...the individuals that I had an interview with, ICE agents, they give you a right, they tell you "Hey, [you] need a lawyer to do this, this is the way to do it." They explain to you the ways, and due process, the ways to stay in the United States, and listen to you.

But these last four years, it's just: "Do you want to sign this paper or not?" Decency, compassion, none of that. I didn't see that. I see that, even jails that I've been, they just drop us off in counties like Morrow County. I'm sorry to tell you this.

All of them, they're racist, and they'll tell you automatically: "Why are you here?" Even sheriff's deputies telling you: "You should get out of here because there will be a war."

Just before I left Morrow County, the Deputy Sheriff told me: "Hey, man. I do not know. You should go home because there's going to be a war...I don't know why you guys want to be in the U.S. You're wasting time because [it's] going to be dangerous here in a couple of months."

GG: Sorry did you say—did you say that he said it's going to be a war? Is that the word you used?

SS: I swear to God. The Sheriff [*Deputy*] told me that.

PART 3

GG: Right now, in Butler County...the sheriff, or the police, or ICE agents, have they been wearing masks in the last few weeks?

SS: In Butler County, here we wear masks. But in Morrow County, we didn't wear masks at all.

GG: Okay. So, at Morrow County, do you think that it's significantly worse, or more dangerous, than Butler County? Or is it essentially the same?

SS: It's a little bit different. Morrow County is worse, because you're surrounded with individuals who're facing time, and some of them are going to prison, and they tell you: "I'll kill you, I don't have nothing to lose, I'm going to prison and I'm about to do fifteen to twenty years." So, you're facing that individual, and also you're facing people who do drugs nonstop. A lot of people overdose, we have to [get someone to] call the ambulance from the street. They overdose on narcotics. Fentanyl, or things that are dangerous, anybody can die from it.

And it's dirty. And, racist, they hate immigrants. They don't like, uh...some of them have never seen a Black man, period, before. So, it's kind of hard, that part. But Butler County, you don't know what's going on because you're locked up in a cell. You only get out, two hours [a day].

So, I don't know how it works here. I know when it comes to the police, they are very hostile. When you say anything, they whoop you.

GG: How often were officials inside the jail physically harassing you and other ICE detainees? Was that a common occurrence?

SS: In Morrow County?

GG: In Morrow County.

SS: Oh God, every day.

PART 4

SS: I grew up in a country where it's half Arabs and half Africans, Mauritania.

GG: Okay.

SS: So, growing up, the law changed dramatically when I was growing up. At age twenty, they just woke up one day and made [Arabic] a language for everybody to speak. Everything changed, the schools have changed, the programs have changed, the government has changed. So Arabs controlled everything, every single thing, starting from administration to law. Even schools now, they...the only way you can continue speaking French, or go to a French school, is to go into private school. The public schools became Arab.

And at the time, because of that, I joined politics and tried to fight against that, because they turned the country to Arabization, and we started fighting. But it was a military-controlled government. And me and my family, and most of the Black [Mauritanians], like myself, ended up being a victim of that horrible timing. I got incarcerated, I did jail time.

GG: You were in politics in Mauritania?

SS: Yeah, I believed in change...standing for equality and justice. I believed in all those things. It was easy to understand, that anybody can be an equal, and slavery would be banned. Because I grew up in a country where—I was born in 1977. All my life...I hate, sometimes, to say it. Because it's a shame to me to talk like this. But I grew up in a country where I thought I was not equal.

PART 5

GG: Do you think [the corrections officers in ICE detention] were at all competent, or keeping people safe in any way?

SS: Absolutely not. The young COs who are from the same county, most of them from Morrow County as well, because when I asked them "How you got this job?" Because I've been seeing young boys like twenty years old, who are racist. And they don't they never saw a Black man. The first time they see immigrants, it's because of ICE. If it wasn't for no ICE, they will never in their life see immigrants. And most of them never even travel, they've never been to a city. So they pretty much just live in that little town, which is a racist town, and they've got different beliefs.

They pretty much, when I talk to them they sound like they believe in God, they're Christian. But they're just too much extreme. It's never what they believe in. They believe in, like, this country belongs to—cause I've been having conversations for a couple of years, and they're open to talk about their views, and why they believe. They, first of all, they believe they're here to protect their country.

They'll be telling me that, like: "Yeah, Trump is a good president because he's giving us our stuff back, he's giving us our country back. Because we made a mistake in the 1500s, we also made a mistake in 1985 by letting immigrants come in. But when they come they will never leave, they will take our jobs, they will kill our people, they're bad guys." And I'll just be listening to them, and they'll be meaning what they're saying because of the way they treat us....

One day, I remember, it was a guy from Mexico who was beat up by some state inmate in the bathroom. And when I tried, uh—I was a witness, and when they wanted my statement, they [were] scared of me, saying—"If you say anything about what's going on here, you're out of here yourself, yourself is gone." So, you cannot—and the COs are watching that, and they don't care. They're not gonna help you about it. So the COs are pretty much part of that conspiracy. A clique of friends. But they don't care about immigrants. Because usually they don't last, they are there only for ninety days, and then deported. So, nobody never heard about their stories, and how they've been treated, because most of them got deported. But I watched, and I saw multiple individuals physically assaulted.

And I saw a guy also was physically assaulted by ICE. And I witnessed it, he was bleeding because he refused to go back [to be deported]. They tried to take him to the airport to deport him. And he said he ain't going, because they're gonna kill him when he goes home. And he was wrestling, doing things with ICE, and they end up beating him up. He came back actually bleeding, and I asked him: "What happened?"

He said they beat him up. I wanted to call people to help him, I wanted to call the outside world. Even my daughter's mom, and people that I knew that might put things on Facebook or stuff like that.

But I was not able to do so because they removed him and he ended up being deported on a charter flight two weeks after that. And I never had a chance to get anything from it. COs know about it, COs do the same. They fight you, they gang beat you up. They watch state inmates beat immigrants up, they don't care about it. And, some people don't speak English, most of the immigrants who cross the border, who end up being in ICE custody, don't speak English.

PART 6

SS: [*What*] I saw in ICE custody from 2017 to 2018, it's horrible, and it's inhumane. And it was done by professional people who represent a state, or people who represent a federal government. And that's something that I will...I will not stop talking about. And I understand it was just a bad person who's lucky to get a job, and they abuse their authority. And they did things that they shouldn't, though, that is unequal, and inhumane. But, I had nobody to talk to at the time. But I'm glad I talked to you. And I'm glad that you're listening to what I'm telling you as well.

GG: It's really, really a privilege to talk to you... I feel I'm so lucky that you're the person I got on the phone.

AUTOMATED RESPONSE: *This call will be terminated in one minute.*

SS: I'm still in quarantine. So, the regulations is, you have only an hour to get out and call people so I decided to make this phone call and I wanted to talk to you as well.

But it is the timing, we lock down twenty-two hours, then we only get out for two hours. So it's still a hard time, and we just hope that one day, hopefully we see the light. It's still tough. It's still tough, but we just have hope, maybe one day things might change. And I'm confident that's something—I don't know, maybe, I hope I'm right, but things might change.

GG: I hope you're right too.

Journey and Hope Continuing
Bol Aweng

ABOUT THE ILLUSTRATOR

Eldis Rodriguez-Baez (b. 1970, Cuba) is a graduate from the ESNECA Business School (2020), Spain, with a Master's in Interior Design, and from the University of Havana (1992) with a Bachelor of Arts in Foreign Language and Literature. He spent his childhood, youth, and a great part of his adult life in his native Cuba. Before his relocation to the United States in 2009, to live and work, he traveled throughout South America for almost a decade. Rodriguez-Baez' works are now part of private collections in the United States, as well as Canada, Switzerland, Cuba, Chile, Spain, Costa Rica, Mexico, and Peru.

Being away from his country and its people filled Mr. Rodriguez-Baez with emotions he wouldn't have felt otherwise. Painting is an escape back to his memories, a way of bringing the colors of Havana back to life in his heart and imagination. Mr. Rodriguez-Baez formerly worked as an educator in the Cleveland area.

AFTERWORD

The Ohio Immigrant Alliance is sponsored by Anacaona LLC, a communications firm. Anacaona was a Taína warrior who used diverse tactics to try to protect her people from colonizers, and she is one of my heroes. We know about Anacaona today because her story was passed down through generations. Storytelling is central to human existence. Recounting narratives is how we preserve history, build empathy, and teach values to our children.

Sometimes the stories we tell are inaccurate. They obscure truth, recast immoral actors as heroes, and manipulate thinking. This is true for much of the "history" we were taught as children about the creation of the United States. On the one hand, we were told to embrace values like equality and self-determination. On the other, our elders refused to admit our true histories, and the many times people failed to live up to these standards.

If we don't acknowledge our failures and learn from our past, how do we build a more just future?

Storytelling helps us find commonalities and understand each other. Like storytelling, migration is a shared human experience. Even if you have always lived in the same place, you have something in common with a person who was forced to flee her home, or a person who decided to move for new opportunities. And if you came from somewhere else, you have something in common with a person who has always lived where they always lived.

"Far from their eyes" doesn't have to be a permanent state. We hope you learned something about yourself and others in Volume I of the Ohio Migration Anthology.

—Lynn Tramonte and Awa Harouna

CONNECT WITH US

The Ohio Migration Anthology was produced by the Ohio Immigrant Alliance (OHIA), a group of immigrants and citizens working together to make Ohio a more welcoming place for immigrants. Find us on Facebook (https://bit.ly/FacebookOHIA), Instagram (https://bit.ly/InstagramOHIA), and Twitter (https://twitter.com/tramontela). Join our email list at https://ohioimmigrant.org/. Donate to our work (via Anacaona, LLC) at https://bit.ly/AnacaonaForOHIA.

A free reflection and creation guide is available to all who want to delve deeper into the themes of this book and take their own journey. Just answer a few questions and receive a copy in your inbox. Go to https://bit.ly/OMASurvey.

A portion of the sales of this book will benefit the Ohio Center for Strategic Immigration Litigation & Outreach (OCSILiO) and the Cleveland Association of Black Storytellers (CABS). OCSILiO provides free legal services to immigrants in Ohio immigration jails as they fight to win their deportation cases. CABS is dedicated to the preservation and proliferation of the African Oral Tradition, the root of Blackstorytelling throughout the diaspora. Learn more about them at https://ocsilio.org/ and https://clevelandstorytellers.org/.

Contributors to *Far From Their Eyes: Ohio Migration Anthology, Volume I* serve their communities through their art and various other initiatives. Below are just a few.

Read about the **Buckeye Clinic in South Sudan, founded by Bol Aweng**, at https://buckeyeclinic.org/. Find Bol's books *The Journey of Hope* (author/illustrator) and *Maluak's Cows* (Maluak Chol author, Bol Aweng illustrator), on Goodreads.

George Shadrack Kamanda's manifesto, *Citizenship Reimagined: The Case for a Responsible Whole Citizenry in Sierra Leone*, is also available on Goodreads.

Get involved in the work of the **Mauritanian Network for Human Rights in US,** and support their mission, at https://www.mauritanian-network.org/.

Sony Ton-Aime's chapbook, *La Womann*, was published by Ironworks Press (2019). Read more about the **ID13 Prison Literacy Project** at https://www.id13project.com/.

Read "Inside Morrow County Jail: How a rural Ohio jail became the epicenter of the immigration crisis," by **Grace Goldstein with Saidu Sow,** at https://www.thecollegianmagazine.com/inside-morrow-county-jail/ (The Kenyon Collegian, March 2021).

View new paintings and additional works from **artist Eldis Rodriguez-Baez** at http://havanacolors.com/.

If you enjoyed this book, please give us a five-star rating and review on Goodreads, Amazon, and other book-seller websites. Tell your friends, family members, and network about *Far From Their Eyes:*

Ohio Migration Anthology, Volume I. Help us spread the message that we are all just people, with equal worth and dreams.

Libraries, book clubs, reporters, educators, and community groups seeking additional information about the anthology and events can contact admin@ohioimmigrant.org. Potential submissions for Volume II may also be sent to admin@ohioimmigrant.org.

Thank you for joining us on this "journey of hope" with *Far From Their Eyes: Ohio Migration Anthology, Volume I.*

Editor's Note

I'd like to honor all of the Ohioans who contributed their stories and experiences to this anthology. It is not easy to let the world in, to watch as you struggle through some of the most difficult times of your life. Your bravery is a gift. It helps others feel less alone and educates those who never lived these experiences.

I'd also like to thank Shari Nacson and Kevin Tasker for their early editing and ideas; Awa Harouna for bringing this whole manuscript together; and Lisa Bess Kramer for her advice, experience, connections, and unwavering positivity.

Marlene Tramonte for supporting every endeavor I have engaged in, every time. Claudia Longo and Maryam Sy for being the best of friends and co-conspirators. Anne Tramonte for always having my back, making me laugh, and bringing back the scat.

Rafael, Lucia, Colten, and Mary for being the reasons.

—Lynn Tramonte

CPSIA information can be obtained
at www.ICGtesting.com
Printed in the USA
BVHW021838030921
616024BV00016B/609